Hormone Research

International Journal of Experimental and Clinical Endocrinology
Founded 1970 as 'Hormones' by M. Marois

General Information

Publication data: 'Hormone Research' is published 12 times annually. Volumes 29–30 with 6 issues each appear in 1988

Subscription rates: Subscriptions run for a full calendar year. Prices are given per volume, surface postage included.

Personal subscription: SFr. 224.–, US$ 149.10. (Must be in the name of, billed to, and paid by an individual. Order must be marked 'personal subscription'.)

Institutional subscription: SFr. 320.–, US$ 213.00. (Regular rate.)

Members of the European Society of Paediatric Endocrinology: SFr. 64.–, US$ 42.60. Lawson Wilkins Society; Schweizerische Gesellschaft für Endokrinologie: SFr. 192.–, US$ 127.00.

Airmail postage: SFr. 35.–, US$ 24.00. (Extra per volume.)

Microform subscription: SFr. 160.–, US$ 106.50. (Available exclusively to subscribers of the paper edition.)

Single issues and back volumes: Information on availability and prices can be obtained through the Publisher.

Subscription orders: Orders can be placed at agencies, bookstores, directly with the Publisher S. Karger AG, P.O. Box, CH – 4009 Basel (Switzerland) or with any of the following distributors:
Deutschland, West-Berlin, Ost-Europa, Naher Osten: S. Karger GmbH, Postfach 1724, D – 8034 Germering/München
France: Librairie Luginbühl, 36, bd de Latour-Maubourg, F – 75007 Paris
Great Britain: John Wiley and Sons, Ltd., Baffins Lane, Chichester, Sussex, PO19 1UD
USA: S. Karger Publishers, Inc., 79 Fifth Avenue, New York, NY 10003
India, Bangladesh, Sri Lanka: S. Karger India Subscription Agency, B – 5/132 Safdarjung Enclave, New Delhi-110029
Japan, South Korea: Katakura Libri, Inc., 36-9 Hongo 3-chome, Bunkyo-ku, Tokyo 113

Change of address: Both old and new address should be stated and sent to the subscription source.

KARGER

Bibliographic indices: This journal is regularly listed in bibliographic services, including *Current Contents®*.

Book Reviews: Books are accepted for review by special agreement.

Advertising: Correspondence and rate requests should be addressed to the Publisher.

Hormone Res.
Printed in Switzerland

S. Karger AG,
Postfach, CH – 4009 Basel (Schweiz)

Erscheint 12mal jährlich

Hormone Research

'Hormone Research' aims to provide rapid publication of clinical investigations and case reports, as well as experimental and methodological work related to endocrinology. Correspondence is welcome, but publication of letters is at the discretion of the editors.

Submission: Only original papers written in English are considered and should be sent to:

Prof. J. Girard
Universitäts-Kinderklinik Basel
Römergasse 8
CH – 4005 Basel (Switzerland)

Manuscripts should be submitted in triplicate (with three sets of illustrations of which one is an original), typewritten double-spaced on one side of the paper, with a wide margin.

Conditions: All manuscripts are subject to editorial review. Manuscripts are received with the explicit understanding that they are not under simultaneous consideration by any other publication. Submission of an article for publication implies the transfer of the copyright from the author to the publisher upon acceptance. Accepted papers become the permanent property of 'Hormone Research' and may not be reproduced by any means, in whole or in part, without the written consent of the publisher. It is the author's responsibility to obtain permission to reproduce illustrations, tables, etc. from other publications.

Arrangement:

Title page: The first page of each paper should indicate the title (main title underlined), the authors' names, and the institute where the work was conducted. A short title for use as running head is also required.

Key words: For indexing purposes, a list of 3–10 key words in English is essential.

Abstract: Each paper needs an abstract of up to 10 lines.

Small type: Paragraphs which can or must be set in smaller type (case histories, test methods, etc.) should be indicated with a 'p' (petit) in the margin on the left-hand side.

Footnotes: Avoid footnotes. When essential, they are numbered consecutively and typed at the foot of the appropriate page.

Tables and illustrations: Tables (numbered in Roman numerals) and illustrations (numbered in Arabic numerals) should be prepared on separate sheets. Tables require a heading, and figures a legend, also prepared on a separate sheet. For the reproduction of illustrations, only good drawings and original photographs can be accepted; negatives or photocopies cannot be used. When possible, group several illustrations on one block for reproduction (max. size 140 × 188 mm) or provide crop marks. On the back of each illustration, indicate its number, the author's name, and 'top'. Color illustrations are reproduced at the author's expense.

References: In the text identify references by Arabic numerals [in square brackets]. Material submitted for publication but not yet accepted should be noted as 'unpublished data' and not be included in the reference list. The list of references should include only those publications which are cited in the text. Do not alphabetize; number references in the order in which they are first mentioned in the text. The surnames of the authors followed by initials should be given. There should be no punctuation other than a comma to separate the authors. When there are more than 3 authors, the names of the first 3 only are used, followed by 'et al'. Abbreviate journal names according to the Index Medicus system. (Also see International Committee of Medical Journal Editors: Uniform requirements for manuscripts submitted to biomedical journals. Ann Intern Med 1982;96: 766–771.)

Examples

(a) Papers published in periodicals: Kauffman HF, van der Heide S, Beaumont F, et al: Class-specific antibody determination against *Aspergillus fumigatus* by means of the enzyme-linked immunosorbent assay. III. Comparative study: IgG, IgA, IgM ELISA titers, precipitating antibodies and IgE binding after fractionation of the antigen. Int Arch Allergy Appl Immunol 1986; 80:300–306.

(b) Monographs: Matthews DE, Farewell VT: Using and Understanding Medical Statistics. Basel, Karger, 1985.

(c) Edited books: Hardy WD Jr, Essex M: FeLV-induced feline acquired immune deficiency syndrome: A model for human AIDS; in Klein E (ed): Acquired Immunodeficiency Syndrome. Prog Allergy. Basel, Karger, 1986, vol 37, pp 353–376.

Full address: The exact postal address complete with postal code of the senior author must be given. If correspondence is handled by someone else, indicate this accordingly.

Further details: Authors may consult our leaflet 'Rules for the Preparation of Manuscripts', available on request from the Publisher, S. Karger AG, P.O. Box, CH – 4009 Basel (Switzerland).

Page charges: There is no page charge for papers of 4 or fewer printed pages (including tables, illustrations and references). Each additional complete or partial page is charged to the author at SFr. 415.– / US$ 275.00. The allotted size of a paper is equal to approx. 12 manuscript pages (including tables, illustrations and references).

Galley proofs: Unless indicated otherwise, galley proofs are sent to the first-named author and should be returned with the least possible delay. Alterations made in galley proofs, other than the correction of printer's errors, are charged to the author. No page proofs are supplied.

Reprints: Order forms and a price list are sent with the galley proofs. Orders submitted after the issue is printed are subject to considerably higher prices. Allow five weeks from date of publication for delivery of reprints.

KARGER

EUROPEAN
NEUROENDOCRINE
ASSOCIATION

Somatostatin

Recent Advances in Basic Research and Clinical Applications

An International Symposium of the European Neuroendocrine Association Madrid, October 7–8, 1986

Guest Editors:
E. del Pozo, Berne
A. Gómez-Pan, Madrid

38 figures, 14 tables, 1988

KARGER

S. Karger · Medical and Scientific Publishers · Basel · München · Paris · London · New York · New Delhi · Singapore · Tokyo · Sydney

Drug Dosage

The authors and the publisher have exerted every effort to ensure that drug selection and dosage set forth in this text are in accord with current recommendations and practice at the time of publication. However, in view of ongoing research, changes in government regulations, and the constant flow of information relating to drug therapy and drug reactions, the reader is urged to check the package insert for each drug for any change in indications and dosage and for added warnings and precautions. This is particularly important when the recommended agent is a new and/or infrequently employed drug.

Printed in Switzerland by Thür AG Offsetdruck, Pratteln
ISBN 3-8055-4809-5

Contents

Preface

Natural somatostatin has been characterized as an important regulator of central and peripheral endocrine functions. The availability of new potent derivatives with prolonged action has stimulated the interest of scientists in experimental and clinical aspects of this family of inhibitory peptides. Moreover, the variety of actions exerted by one and the same substance has encouraged the search for analogs with more selective actions.

The purpose of the meeting held October 7–8, 1986, in Madrid, and sponsored by the European Neuroendocrine Association, was to present and discuss recent developments in somatostatin research. In a first part, the structure-function relationships, mechanisms of action, receptor specificity, methods of detection, and physiological aspects were illustrated. This was followed by an overview of the possible clinical applications of somatostatins and a detailed assessment of the therapeutic scope of these peptides. Thus, the availability of derivatives with prolonged half-lives has permitted the evaluation of chronic treatment with such agents in a series of abnormal secretory states, mainly involving the pituitary and gastrointestinal hormones, and also in disturbances of glucose homeostasis. A protective effect on tissue damage has been explored and its effectiveness in the management of gastrointestinal hemorrhage has also been investigated.

The results were encouraging. In acromegaly, prolonged therapy with somatostatin represents a genuine alternative to more conventional medicamentous treatment, and to surgery and irradiation. Its palliative effect has been clearly demonstrated in adenomas and metastasizing tumors of the upper digestive tract. Hyperinsulinism of the newborn can be readily corrected by somatostatin, and instability of glucose control in some diabetics on insulin replacement can also be ameliorated. Although the therapeutic benefit seems to outweigh other effects emanating from the broad spectrum of actions typical of somatostatin, further experimental and galenical developments may favor the wider clinical use of this interesting substance.

J. Girard, Editor

E. del Pozo, A. Gómez-Pan, Guest Editors

Hormone Res. 29: 50–53 (1988)

0301–0163/88/0293–0050$2.75/0

Somatostatin: A Historical Perspective

R. Hall, M.D. Page, C. Dieguez, M.F. Scanlon

Department of Medicine, University of Wales College of Medicine, Heath Park, Cardiff, UK

Key Words. Somatostatin actions · Circulating tissue levels

Abstract. Following the discovery and biochemical characterization of natural somatostatin its action profile has been thoroughly investigated. Although the name somatostatin was coined in virtue of its growth hormone release-inhibiting properties, a number of central and peripheral endocrine and paracrine actions have been ascribed to this peptide. Its inhibitory effect on a series of pituitary and gastrointestinal hormones has characterized somatostatin as a classical brain-gut hormone. Circulating and tissue levels of somatostatin and its possible physiological role are analyzed and clinical implications are drawn.

In 1973 Brazeau et al. [1] isolated a tetradecapeptide from ovine hypothalami which inhibited growth hormone (GH) secretion from cultured anterior pituitary cells. This substance was named growth hormone-release-inhibiting hormone (GH-RIH) but this has since been replaced by the term somatostatin.

Pituitary Actions of Somatostatin

Initial studies focussed on the pituitary actions of somatostatin demonstrated inhibitory actions on the release of several anterior lobe hormones. GH secretion was suppressed in all species tested under both basal and stimulated conditions. A dramatic fall in GH secretion could be observed in acromegaly in response to intravenous somatostatin but this was followed by a rapid rebound of GH release on terminating the infusion, as expected from the short half-life of the compound, thus making any therapeutic application of the native tetradecapeptide impractical.

Thyrotrophin (TSH) secretion was also suppressed by somatostatin both in the basal state and when stimulated by thyrotrophin-releasing hormone (TRH), dopamine antagonists or hypothyroidism. Suppression of secretion was also demonstrated in some TSH-secreting tumours. By using antibodies to somatostatin in rats it was possible to raise basal TSH levels and enhance the cold-induced rise of TSH, implying that somatostatin played a physiological role in the control of TSH secretion. The development of hypothyroidism in some GH-deficient children treated with GH provided indirect evidence that GH might stimulate hypothalamic somatostatin release which then reduced TSH secretion and there appears to be a reciprocal relationship between GH and TSH secretion.

Somatostatin inhibits ACTH release to some extent in some states of hypersecretion such as Nelson's syndrome. It was shown to have no effect on luteinising hormone (LH) but to reduce the slight TRH-induced rise in follicle stimulating hormone secretion. No consistent effects on prolactin (PRL) secretion were observed initially but recent data have demonstrated inhibition of PRL release in vitro from cultures of female but not male rat pituitary cells. Somatostatin also inhibits PRL secretion in normal males treated with oestrogens and in some acromegalic patients. All these pituitary actions of somatostatin have been extensively reviewed elsewhere [2].

Caution was advised on the interpretation of many of the experiments with somatostatin since they involved either pharmacological doses of the compound or studies in pathological states. Examples of the former include infusions of somatostatin in vivo or its incubation with anterior pituitary cells in vitro. Examples of the latter include somatostatin infusions in patients with hormone-secreting tumours such as acromegaly. Such studies need to be distinguished from those using antibodies to somatostatin which do provide physiologically relevant information.

Localisation of Somatostatin

Initial histochemical studies localised somatostatin in the hypothalamus, median eminence, periventricular nucleus, arcuate nucleus and in several extra-hypothalamic areas of the brain [3, 4]. Subsequently, it was located in a variety of sites elsewhere including the D cells of the pancreatic islets, the gastric antrum, the upper intestine, salivary glands and the parafollicular C cells of the thyroid. These findings led to the successful search for actions elsewhere and so far a very wide variety of inhibitory effects of somatostatin has been demonstrated in many different tissues and systems (table I).

These studies revealed a dual role for somatostatin with both endocrine and paracrine actions, examples of the latter being its secretion from the D cells of the pancreatic islet to regulate local production of insulin and glucagon and the action of locally produced somatostatin on gastric acid and gastric secretion. Examples of the former include reduction of GH and TSH secretion by the pituitary.

Table I. Inhibitory actions of somatostatin

Tissue	Response
Anterior pituitary	secretion of GH and TSH and occasionally PRL and ACTH
Pancreas (islets)	secretion of insulin, glucagon and pancreatic polypeptide
Pancreas (exocrine)	secretion of water, bicarbonate and enzymes
Stomach	acid and pepsin secretion and gastric emptying
Intestine	amine and peptide hormone secretion, absorption of triglycerides, sugars, amino acids, and other nutrients, mesenteric blood flow
Gall bladder	bile flow
Kidney	renin secretion, aldosterone response to angiotensin II
Parathyroid	parathyroid hormone secretion
Salivary gland	salivary flow
Platelets	aggregation
Neurones	inhibition of firing but sometimes excitation
Thyroid	calcitonin secretion

Forms of Somatostatin

Somatostatin has therefore emerged as a classical brain-gut peptide with a much wider spectrum of actions than was originally anticipated. It is an ancient peptide in evolutionary terms, being present in the single cell protozoan. The mammalian form is identical with that of the angler fish separated in evolution by 4×10^8 years.

By standard molecular biological techniques it has been possible to identify the structure of preprosomatostatin, a 116 amino acid peptide [5, 6]. Tissues contain at least 4 peptides which react with antisera directed against the C-terminus of somatostatin-14 and a further 3 peptides which cross-react with somatostatin-28 [1–12] antisera [6–8].

It is unlikely that these different forms of somatostatin represent extraction artefacts since different forms can be extracted from different tissues. It appears that post-translational processing differs in different tissues [9]. Most parts of the central nervous system, rat retinal cells, pancreatic islet cells and gastrin-producing cells synthesise predominantly somatostatin-14 whereas intestinal mucosa and bovine retina synthesise predominantly somatostatin-28. However, anterior periventricular neurones synthesise equimolar amounts of somatostatin-14 and somatostatin-28 [10]. Furthermore, the median eminence contains a much higher proportion of somatostatin-28 than the rest of the hypothalamus which may well contain different populations of somatostatinergic neurones secreting different molecular forms in response to different signals [11]. It is also clear now that somatostatin-28 and somatostatin-14 exert different biological actions since they display different potency on the inhibition of basal GH, PRL and insulin release and bombesin-stimulated insulin, glucagon and gastrin release [2]. Finally, somatostatin-28 does not inhibit rabbit platelet aggregation whereas somatostatin-14 does cause this effect although not as potently as somatostatin 15–28 [12].

Mechanisms of Action of Somatostatin

Somatostatin binds to a specific membrane receptor and inhibits adenyl cyclase activity through linkage with a N_i unit, having an opposing effect to growth hormone-releasing hormone (GRH) which stimulates adenyl cyclase by coupling with an N_s unit. Somatostatin also has effects independent of its action on cAMP leading to a fall in intracellular calcium which reduces hormone secretion, possibly via increasing cell permeability to K^+ which causes membrane hyperpolarisation.

A further problem which remains to be resolved is the existence of separate binding sites for the different forms of somatostatin. Studies of binding in the presence of different concentrations of calcium and those based on the effects of GTP and on autoradiography suggest, but as yet do not prove, that separate binding sites exist [13].

Plasma, Brain and CSF Somatostatin Levels

There are many reports of alterations in plasma levels of somatostatin basally and in response to various stimuli in normal and disease states. However, with the exception of hypophyseal portal somatostatin there is no firm evidence whatsoever for a general endocrine role for somatostatin and the physiological relevance of these findings must remain questionable at present.

Increased circulating somatostatin levels may be found in a variety of hormone producing tumours most notably pancreatic and duodenal somatostatinomas which may present with mild diabetes mellitus and gallstones, but also gastrinomas, vipomas, glucagonomas, insulinomas, medullary thyroid carcinoma, phaeochromocytoma, thyroid carcinoma and lung carcinoid tumours. In acromegaly, normal basal and meal stimulated somatostatin levels, as well as normal CSF levels have been reported. Patients with type I diabetes mellitus show an exaggerated somatostatin response to food but a normal response to hypoglycaemia whereas type II diabetics show either normal or reduced responses to food and a reduced response to hypoglycaemia. It should be emphasised once again that the precise physiological or pathophysiological relevance of many of these observations remains obscure. However, measurement of plasma somatostatin does have a place in screening for endocrine tumours and in the follow-up of patients with such tumours during treatment.

It has also proved possible to demonstrate marked differences in brain and CSF somatostatin levels in patients with a variety of neurological or neuropsychiatric disorders. Brain somatostatin levels are reduced in Alzheimer's disease (particularly frontal and temporal cortex and hippocampus), schizophrenia (particularly frontal cortex), Parkinson's disease with dementia and multiple sclerosis [14–16]. Levels are increased in the nucleus accumbens in patients with Huntington's chorea [17]. CSF somatostatin levels, although normal in Huntington's chorea, are reduced in schizophrenia, major depression, Parkinson's disease and multiple sclerosis, usually in parallel with the brain levels [15, 18]. The mechanisms underlying these alterations and their pathophysiological significance are unclear but such data provide the basis for hypothetical discussion and further investigation.

Analogues of Somatostatin

A wide variety of somatostatin analogues have been synthesised in an effort to alter the specificity of its biological activity and to prolong its duration of action. These include the potent hexapeptide agonist of Veber et al. [19], a cyclic pentapeptide with antagonistic activity from Fries et al. [20] and most importantly SMS 201-995, a long-acting analogue with a relatively selective action on GH produced by Bauer et al. [21]. The clinical application of these agents will be the subject of a series of contributions within this symposium.

References

1 Brazeau, P.; Vale, W.; Burgus, R.; Ling, N.; Butcher, M.; Rivier, J.; Guillemin, R.: Hypothalamic paptide that inhibits the secretion of immunoreactive pituitary growth hormone. Science *179:* 77–79 (1973).

2 Wass, J.A.H.: Growth hormone neuroregulation and the clinical relevance of somatostatin, in Clinics in endocrinology and metabolism, pp. 695–724 (Saunders, London 1983).

3 Arimura, A.; Sato, H.; Coy, D.H.; Schally, A.V.: Radioimmunoassay for GH-release inhibiting hormone. Proc. Soc. exp. Biol. Med. *148:* 748–749 (1975).

4 Hokfelt, T.; Efendic, S.; Hellerstrom, C.; Johansson, O.; Luft, R.; Arimura, A.: Cellular localization of somatostatin in endocrine-like cells and neurons of the rat, with special references to the A_1-cells of the pancreatic islets and to the hypothalamus. Acta endocr., Copenh. *80:* suppl. 200, pp. 3–41 (1975).

5 Shen, L.-P.; Pictet, R.L.; Rutter, W.J.: Human somatostatin, I. Sequence of the cDNA. Proc. natn. Acad. Sci. USA *79:* 4575–4579 (1982).

6 Goodman, R.H.; Aron, D.C.; Roos, B.A.: Rat-preprosomatostatin: structure and processing by microsomal membranes. J. biol. Chem. *258:* 5570–5573 (1983).

7 Benoit, R.; Ling, N.: Alford, B.; Guillemin, R.: Seven peptides derived from pre-somatostatin in rat brain. Biochem. biophys. Res. Commun. *107:* 944–950 (1982).

8 Benoit, R.; Bohlen, P.; Esch, F.; Ling, N.: Neuropeptides derived from prosomatostatin that do not contain the somatostatin-14 sequence. Brain Res. *311:* 23–29 (1984).

9 Low, M.J.; Hammer, R.E.; Goodman, R.H.; Habener, J.F.; Palmiter, R.D.; Brinster, R.L.: Tissue-specific post-translational

processing of pre-prosomatostatin encoded by a metallothionein-somatostatin fusion gene in transgenic mice. Cell *41:* 211–219 (1985).
10 Harmar, A.J.; Pierotti, A.R.; Ligthman, S.L.: Somatostatin; in Neuroendocrinology, pp. 389–408 (Blackwell, London 1986).
11 Lewis, M.D.; Foord, S.M.; Lewis, M.B.; Hall, R.; Scanlon, M.F.: Differential production of SRIF 14 and 28 by fetal rat hypothalamic cells separated by velocity sedimentation. Neuroendocrinology *44:* 125–131 (1986).
12 Fuse, I.; Ito, S.; Takagi, A.; Shibata, A.: Different effects of three kinds of somatostatin (15–28, 1–14, 1–28) on rabbit's platelet aggregation. Life Sci. *36:* 2047–2052 (1985).
13 Srikant, C.B.; Patel, Y.C.: Somatostatin receptors: evidence for functional and structural heterogeneity; in Reichlin, Somatostatin, Basic and clinical status, pp. 89–102 (Plenum Press, New York 1987).
14 Rossor, M.N.; Iversen, L.L.; Reynolds, G.P.; Mountjoy, C.Q.; Roth, M.: Neurochemical characteristics of early and late onset types of Alzheimer's disease. Clin. Res. *288:* 961–964 (1984).
15 Agid, Y.; Javoy-Agid, F.: Peptides and Parkinson's disease. Trends. Neurosci. *1985:* 30–35.
16 Price, D.L.: New perspectives on Alzheimers disease. Annu. Rev. Neurosci. *9:* 489–512 (1986).
17 Nemeroff, C.B.; Youngblood, W.W.; Manberg, P.J.; Prange, A.J., Jr.; Kizer, J.L.: Regional brain concentrations of neuropeptides in Huntington's chorea and schizophrenia. Science *221:* 972–975 (1983).
18 Rubinow, D.R.; Post, R.M.; Davis, C.; Doran, A.: Somatostatin and depression; in Reichlin, Somatostatin, Basic and clinical status, pp. 183–192 (Plenum Press, New York 1987).
19 Veber, D.F.; Freidinger, R.M.; Perlow, D.S.; Palevata, W.J.; Holly, F.W.; Strachan, R.G.; Nutt, R.F.; Arison, B.H.; Homnick, C.; Randall, W.C.; Glitzer, M.S.; Saperstein, R.; Hirschman, R.: A potent cyclic hexapeptide analogue of somatostatin. Nature, Lond. *292:* 55–58 (1981).
20 Fries, J.L.; Murphy, W.A.; Sueiras-Diaz, J.; Coy, D.H.: Somatostatin antagonist analog increases growth hormone, insulin and glucagon release in the rat. Peptides *3:* 811–814 (1982).
21 Bauer, W.; Briner, U.; Doepfner, W.; Haller, R.; Huguenin, R.; Marbach, P.; Petcher, T.J.; Pless, J.: SMS 201–995. A very potent and selective octapeptide analogue of somatostatin with prolonged action. Life Sci. *31:* 1133–1140 (1982).

Dr. R. Hall
Department of Medicine
University of Wales College of Medicine
Heath Park
Cardiff (UK)

Hormone Res. *29:* 54–58 (1988)

Structure-Function Relationships of Somatostatin Analogs

P. Marbach, W. Bauer, U. Briner, W. Döpfner, T. Petcher, J. Pless

Preclinical Research Department, Sandoz Ltd., Basle, Switzerland

Key Words. Somatostatin · Structure · Duration of action · Specificity · Analogs

Abstract. Objective of peptide chemistry has always been the production of analogues for clinical application. Advantages sought over natural peptides are (a) reduced molecular size; (b) prolonged biological half-life, and (c) enhanced specificity. After elucidation of the active core of somatostatin a number of analogues have been synthetized. Among them SMS 201-995, an octapeptide, was selected for further development because of its high potency and prolonged plasma clearance. Procedures extending the duration of action of somatostatin derivatives such as enhancement of lipophilicity and amino acid substitution are described, and factors influencing the specificity of such substances are succinctly analyzed.

The goal of all peptide chemists involved in somatostatin (SRIF) research has always been to create analogs of clinical utility. These should therefore have three important advantages over natural somatostatin: (a) reduced size because of economical synthesis; (b) prolonged biological half-life, and (c) enhanced specificity. The following sections will be concerned with the analysis of these particular features.

Analogs with Reduced Structure

Figure 1a depicts the potencies of analogs with systematic exchange of single amino acids by the simplest *L*-amino acid, alanin, according to Vale et al. [1]. It demonstrates that the central part of the ring structure seems to be most susceptible to change. Figure 1b shows the replacement of *L*-amino acids by the respective *D*-isomers. These replacements do not change any physicochemical parameters of the side chains. However, they do modify the tertiary structure by distortions in the backbone, consequently disturbing potential hydrogen bonds, beta-turns and other stabilizing features. The important finding in this series was the outstanding activity of the *D*-Trp analog even in this in vitro biological test system. *D*-Trp^8-SRIF was the first superactive analog and this modification became the most copied replacement in future analog designs [2].

Vale et al. [3] consistently pursued the minimal essential sequence of the peptide. The essential part of the sequence, Phe^6-Lys^9, was kept constant and amino acid by amino acid was omitted systematically until they arrived at the octapeptide Cys-Phe-Phe-*D*-Trp-Lys-Thr-Phe-Cys-NH_2. This analog still had 4% of the GH-lowering activity in vitro and a reasonable in vivo activity. Further reduction of the sequence was then deleterious.

Other laboratories also made very important contributions to the design of SRIF analogs with reduced structures [4–6]. Thus, Veber et al. [5] tried, with the aid of computer modelling, to minimize and optimize the structure of SRIF, which led to highly active cyclic hexapeptide analogs. Interestingly enough, these authors omitted the Phe^6 residue, a side chain which was previously thought to be essential. Our group followed another strategy to obtain active SRIF analogs with

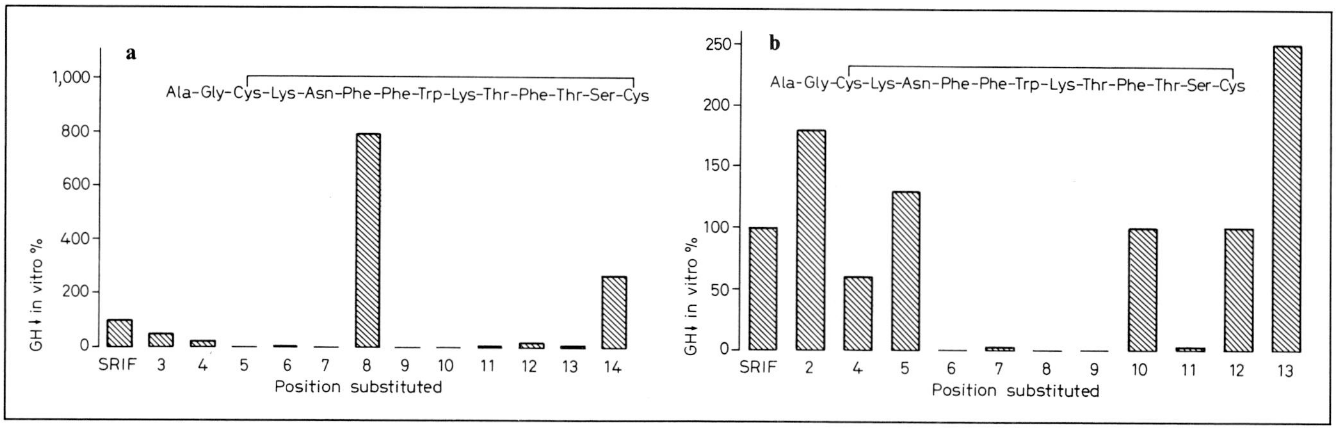

Fig. 1. **a** Potencies of alanine substituted SRIF analogs. **b** Relative potencies of *D*-amino acid substituted somatostatin analogs [1].

Table I. N^{α}-acylated SRIF analogs: R-*D*-Phe-Cys-Phe-*D*-Trp-Lys-Thr-Cys-Thr-ol: GH inhibition in the rat

R	Code Name	ED_{50}, µg/kg, time after application 1 h	6 h	Ratio ED_{50} (6 h) / ED_{50} (1 h)	Activity in vitro (SRIF = 1)
H–	SMS 201-995	0.084	15	179	3
CH_3–CO–		0.6	290	483	3
CH_3–$(CH_2)_4$–CO–		0.26	25	96	0.77
CH_3–$(CH_2)_6$–CO–		3.0	10	3.3	0.55
CH_3–$(CH_2)_7$–CO–		2.8	20	7	1.29
CH_3–$(CH_2)_8$–CO–	203-306	10	16	1.6	1.36
CH_3–$(CH_2)_{10}$–CO–		82	16	0.2	0.42
CH_3–$(CH_2)_{12}$–CO–		54	19	0.35	0.25

reduced structures. This was a stepwise incorporation of additional structural elements of the natural peptide to the minimal essential sequence. This procedure led to the synthesis of SMS 201-995, *D*-Phe-Cys-Phe-*D*-Trp-Lys-Thr-Cys-Thr-ol [7]. In this peptide, also known as Sandostatin, the tetrapeptide sequence 7–10 of SRIF is conformationally stabilized by cyclization with cystin. The *D*-Phe is able to occupy at least part of the conformational space available to Phe^6 in SRIF. The Thr^8, stabilized against metabolic degradation by reducing it to the alcohol, can in its *L*-isomeric form mimic the Thr which was originally at position 12 in SRIF. Sandostatin is in vitro about 2–3 times more active in inhibiting GH secretion in GRF-stimulated primary cell cultures from rat pituitaries. Due to the important improvement in metabolic stability, the in vivo activity is much higher as will be discussed later and elsewhere in this symposium.

Duration of Action

One important drawback for the clinical application of natural SRIF is its very short biological half-life which is in the range of 1–2 min. Structure-activity relationships, where function means duration of action, are therefore of great practical importance.

Sandostatin already has a markedly prolonged biological stability which results in an elimination half-life of about 2 h after subcutaneous application in man [8].

In attempts to further improve the analogs' duration of action, two strategies were followed. First, we increased the lipophilicity of the peptide which should enhance the depot effect at the injection site after s.c. administration. One possible way to do this was by acylation of the octapeptide Sandostatin at the amino-terminus with fatty acids of different chain lengths [9]. When the inhibitory effect on growth hormone was mea-

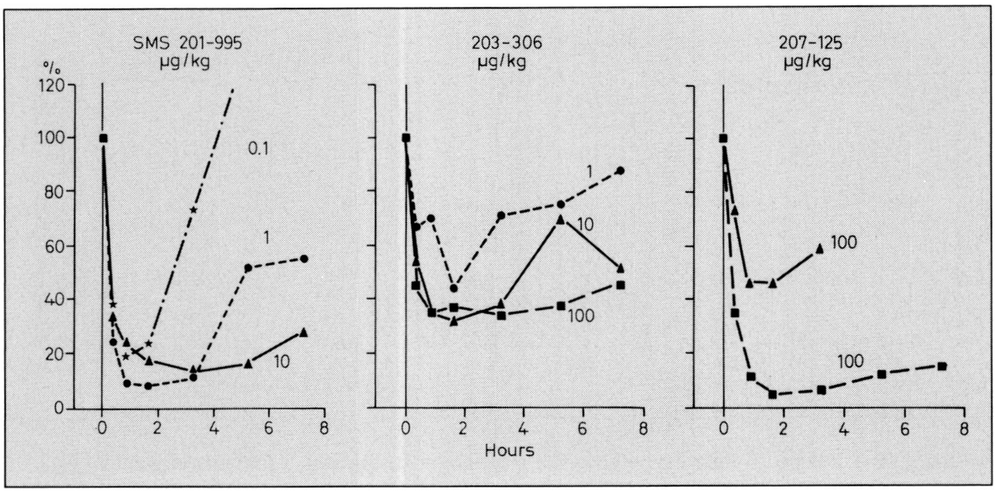

Fig. 2. Inhibition of growth-hormone levels in monkeys after s.c. administration of SRIF analogs.

Table II. Relative Potencies of Specific SRIF Analogs

Peptide	GH (in vitro)	Insulin (in vivo)	Glucagon (in vivo)
SRIF	100	100	100
DesAsn^5-(*D*-Trp^8, *D*-Ser^{13})-	13	1,750	< 1
(*D*-Trp^8, *D*-Cys^{14})-	650	130	1,000
(*D*-Lys^4)-	22	< 1	< 1
DesAsn^{19}(*D*-Trp^{22}, *D*-Ser^{27})-SS28	< 5	14,500	< 100
SMS 201-995	300	300	2,300

sured one hour and six hours after subcutaneous application to male rats, the duration of action could be estimated by the ratio between the two values (table I). Thus, an increase in potency led to a dramatic prolongation of the effect. However, local tolerance was poor, probably through the formation of detergent-like substances. This could be due to the structural features of the analog. Indeed, in vitro hemolysis of erythrocytes was significantly correlated with the chain length of the constituents.

A second approach to analogs with prolonged duration of action is by the design of prodrugs. Reversible substitutions on the amino groups of the lysine side chain should give compounds which would slowly be regenerated after cleavage in the organism. This could be realized by synthesizing Schiff-base derivatives by the condensation of 2-hydroxybenzaldehydes with the lysine side chain. The resulting compounds were stabilized by the formation of a hydrogen bond between the imine-nitrogen and the phenolic hydroxyl group. In the presence of water, however, the Schiff-base product is slowly cleaved to the native compound. The ratio of activities 6 h and 1 h after s.c. application in rats demonstrated that analogs with very high and extremely prolonged activity could be synthesized. Because of the absence of detergent-like structural elements, the compounds were locally well tolerated.

The duration of action was also monitored after single s.c. injections in rhesus monkeys. Figure 2 shows a comparison of the activities of the three most important compounds, Sandostatin, the N$^\alpha$-decanoyl substituted analog 203-306 and the desamino-N$^\varepsilon$-benzhydrilidene derivative 207-125, respectively. The long duration of action on GH secretion can be clearly seen but a superiority of the analogs over SMS 201-995 cannot be demonstrated in this monkey model.

Specificity

A dominant feature of the pharmacology, and perhaps even the physiology of SRIF, is the diversity of actions of this peptide. Most effort was therefore focused on the synthesis of analogs with improved specificity. The early recognized potential application in diabetes makes it desirable to design analogs with greatly diminished inhibiting action on insulin.

In the literature, many analogs have been described to specifically inhibit one or the other hormone. In table II, the activities of a few of them are summarized. The des(Asn^5, *D*-Trp^8, *D*-Ser^{13})-analog shows a very high ratio in favor of insulin inhibition and the (*D*-Trp^8, *D*-Cys^{14})-analog is relatively specific for the inhibition of GH and glucagon.

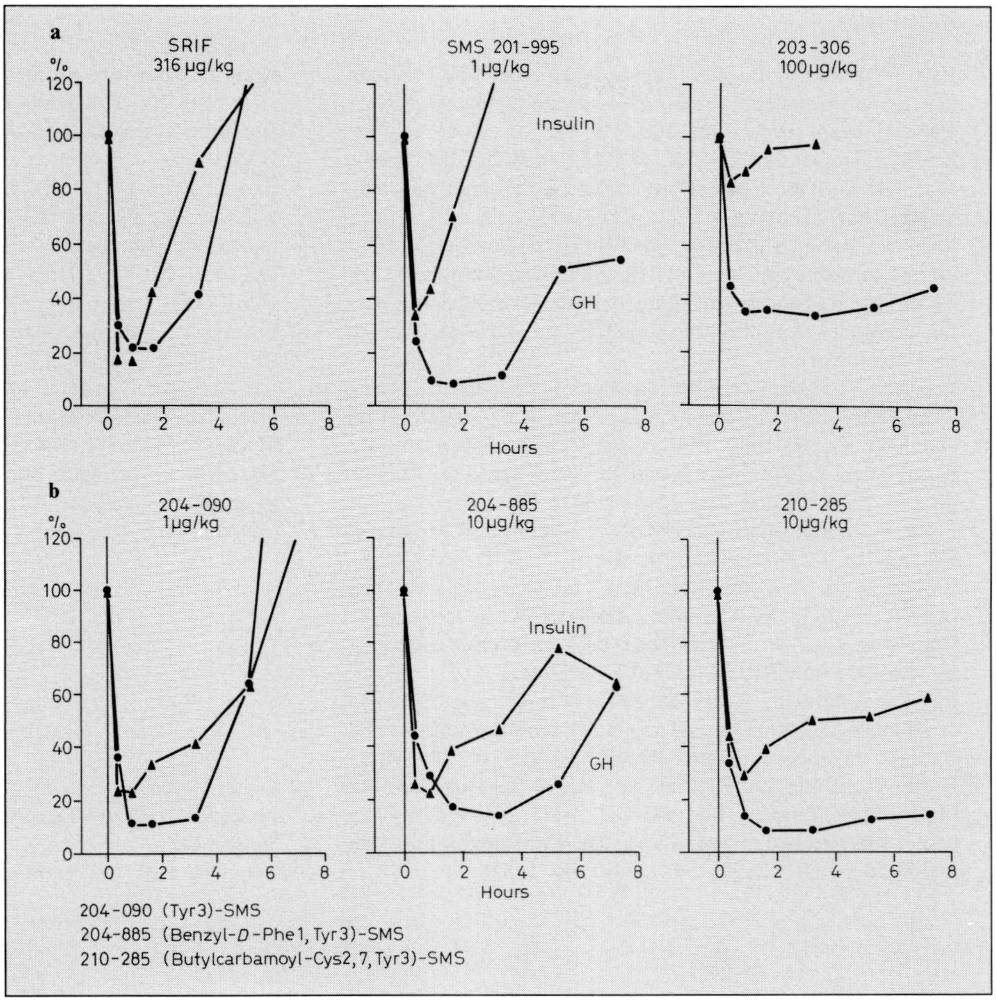

Fig. 3a, b. Specific effects of SRIF analogs in monkeys after s.c. administration.

However, these findings could not be confirmed in clinical trials, probably due to differences in pharmacokinetics [10].

Figure 3 shows the dose-response curves for GH and insulin recorded with different analogs in unstimulated conscious rhesus monkeys in comparison with SRIF. All substances, including natural SRIF, show a more pronounced and longer-lasting inhibitory effect on GH release. The degree of specificity therefore depends on the timing of blood sampling.

Only 203-306, the previously mentioned decanoyl analog of Sandostatin, seems to be truly specific. Tyrosine alone in position 3 or in combination with benzyl at the amino-terminal resulted in very active analogs with a long duration of action. Again the inhibition of insulin was less pronounced. In figure 3b a representative sample of another series of analogs is presented. Noncyclized, reduced SMS 201-995 has been substituted at the sulfhydrils by readily cleavable groups, e.g. tertiary butyloxycarbonyl. Again maximum inhibition of GH lasts longer than maximum inhibition of insulin. The same difference in the pharmacodynamic effects on GH and insulin could also be demonstrated with Sandostatin in man [11].

Perhaps the most striking example of how dependent the specificity of SRIF is on the experimental design could be shown when the effect of Sandostatin was tested in the reversed hemolytic plaque assay with pituitary cells from estrogen-treated male rats [Marbach, Leong, Thorner, unpubl.]. Whereas Sandostatin has no effect on prolactin secretion in cells from normal rat pituitaries, the analog was highly potent and dose-dependently active on the prolactin release of pituitary cells from estradiol-treated rats. Thus, environmental factors and tissue pretreatment are also important requisites in the evaluation of the action profile of these peptides.

References

1 Vale, W.; Rivier, J.; Ling, N.; Brown, M.: Biologic and immunologic activities and applications of somatostatin analogs. Metabolism *27:* suppl. 1, pp. 1391–1401 (1978).

2 Rivier, J.; Brown, M.; Vale, W.: *D*-Trp^8-somatostatin: an analog of somatostatin more potent than the native molecule. Biochem. biophys. Res. Commun. *65:* 746–751 (1975).

3 Vale, W.; Rivier, C.; Brown, M.; Rivier, J.: Pharmacology of thyrotropin releasing factor (TRF), luteinizing hormone-releasing factor (LRF) and somatostatin; in Porter, Hypothalamic peptide hormones and pituitary regulations, pp. 123–126 (Plenum Press, New York 1977).

4 Veber, D.F.; Freidinger, R.M.; Schwenk Perlow, D.; Paleweda, W.J.; Holly, F.W.; Strachan, R.G.; Nutt, R.F.; Arison, B.H.; Homnick, C.; Randall, W.C.; Glitzer, M.S.; Saperstein, R.; Hirschmann, R.: A potent cyclic hexapeptide analogue of somatostatin. Nature, Lond. *292:* 55–58 (1981).

5 Veber, D.F.; Saperstein, R.; Nutt, R.F.; Freidinger, R.M.; Brady, S.F.; Curley, P.; Perlow, D.S.; Paleweda, W.J.; Dylion Colton, C.; Zacchei, A.G.; Tocco, D.J.; Hoff, D.R.; Vandlen, R.L.; Gerich, J.E.; Hall, L.; Mandarino, L.; Cordes E.H.; Anderson, P.S.; Hirschmann, R.: A super active cyclic hexapeptide analog of somatostatin. Life Sci. *34:* 1371–1378 (1984).

6 Buchs, A.; Märki, F.; Keller, U.: Effect of somatostatin and two of its analogues on basal and ariginine-stimulated insulin and glucagon secretion in the dog. Regul. Pept. *4:* 117–126 (1982).

7 Bauer, W.; Briner, U.; Döpfner, W.; Haller, R.; Huguenin, R.; Marbach, P.; Petcher, T.J.; Pless, J.: SMS 201–995. A very potent and selective octapeptide analogue of somatostatin with prolonged action. Life Sci. *31:* 1133–1140 (1982).

8 del Pozo, E.; Neufeld, M.; Schlüter, K.; Tortosa, F.; Clarenbach, P.; Bieder, E.; Wendel, L.; Nüesch, E.; Marbach, P.; Cramer, H.; Kerp, L.: Endocrine profile of a long-acting somatostatin derivative SMS 201–995. Study in normal volunteers following subcutaneous administration. Acta endocr. Copenh. *111:* 433–439 (1986).

9 Bauer, W.; Briner, U.; Döpfner, W.; Haller, R.; Huguenin, R.; Marbach, P.; Petcher, T.J.; Pless, J.: Rational drug design of long-acting somatostatin analogues. 7th Int. Congr. Endocrinology, abstr. No. 139, Congr. Ser. 652. (Excerpta Medica, Amsterdam 1984).

10 Adrian, T.E.; Barnes, A.J.; Long, R.G.; O'Shaughnessy, D.J.; Brown, M.R.; Rivier, J.; Vale, W.; Blackburn, A.M.; Bloom, S.R.: The effect of SRIF analogs on secretion of growth, pancreatic and gastrointestinal hormones in man. J. clin. Endocr. Metab. *53:* 675–681 (1981).

11 Marbach, P.; Neufeld, M.; Pless, J.: Clinical applications of somatostatin analogs. Adv. exp. Med. Biol. *188:* 339–353 (1985).

Dr. P. Marbach
Preclinical Research Department
Sandoz Ltd.
CH-4002 Basle (Switzerland)

Hormone Res. *29:* 59–64 (1988)

0301–0163/88/0293–0059$2.75/0

Mechanism of Action of Somatostatin

M.J. Toro[a], *L. Birnbaumer*[a], *M.C. Redon*[b], *E. Montoya*[b]

[a] Department of Cell Biology, Baylor College of Medicine, Houston, Tex., USA;
[b] Catedra de Bioquimica, Facultad de Ciencias, Universidad de Cadiz, Spain

Key Words. Somatostatin · Internalization · Membrane action · Cytosol

Abstract. The chain of events leading to the manifestation of the biological action of somatostatin are described. Internalization is mediated by cytoskeletal proteins in the presence of calmodulin. Transduction of the somatostatin message at the membrane level takes place through inhibition of cyclic AMP accumulation and blockade of cytosol calcium increases. The influence of central and peripheral factors upon these processes is discussed and the importance of the Ni/Ns components is stressed. Thus, somatostatin also suppresses phosphoinositide turnover and stimulates soluble phosphodiesterase, thus reinforcing its negative effect on cyclase generation.

Somatostatin Internalization

After interaction with the receptor, somatostatin is internalized in a process, which has not as yet been throughly studied, but that should probably be common to polypeptidic hormones and other proteins [1]. This phenomenon has been demonstrated using a somatostatin colloidal gold complex [2]. For other ligands it has been proposed that, after interaction with their receptors, microaggregates of a few occupied receptors are formed. These microaggregates are supposed to fuse into patches leading to the formation of coated pits which are thereafter internalized forming endosomes.

The process of internalization is driven by cytoskeletal proteins, including clathrin and clathrin-associated proteins. For other hypophysiotropic hormones it has been demonstrated that this process requires the calcium acceptor protein calmodulin, and that calmodulin is associated to the formation of coated pits. We have studied the effect of somatostatin and TRH administration to normal rats on pituitary calmodulin subcellular distribution (fig. 1). While TRH does not affect the calmodulin content in the different subcellular fractions, somatostatin increases this protein in membrane and nucleus. We have no explanation for this latter phenomenon; nevertheless, it has been reported that calmodulin increase in membrane fractions is associated with the process of hormone-receptor complex internalization via coated pits [3, 4].

Somatostatin Action at Membrane Level

Two types of action have been classically postulated to be involved in the transduction of somatostatin message, namely the inhibition of adenylyl cyclase and of calcium fluxes. Somatostatin inhibits hormone secretion and cyclic AMP accumulation, mediated by different secretagogues. The multicomponent model of adenylyl cyclase [5–7] (fig. 2) has provided an explanation for this phenomenon. Somatostatin interacts in the anterior pituitary or anterior pituitary-derived cells with receptors coupled to Ni, a component of the cyclase which inhibits the catalytic part of the system. This mechanism was first postulated by Jacobs and co-workers [8, 9] using membranes from S49 cyc-lymphoma cells, which lack the stimulatory (Ns) component, and has been extended to pituitary and pituitary-derived cells. These authors showed that in the presence of guanosine triphosphate

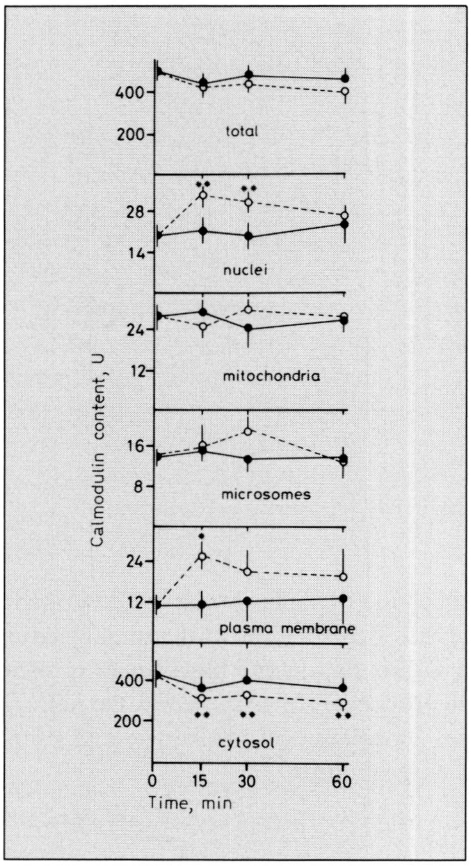

1

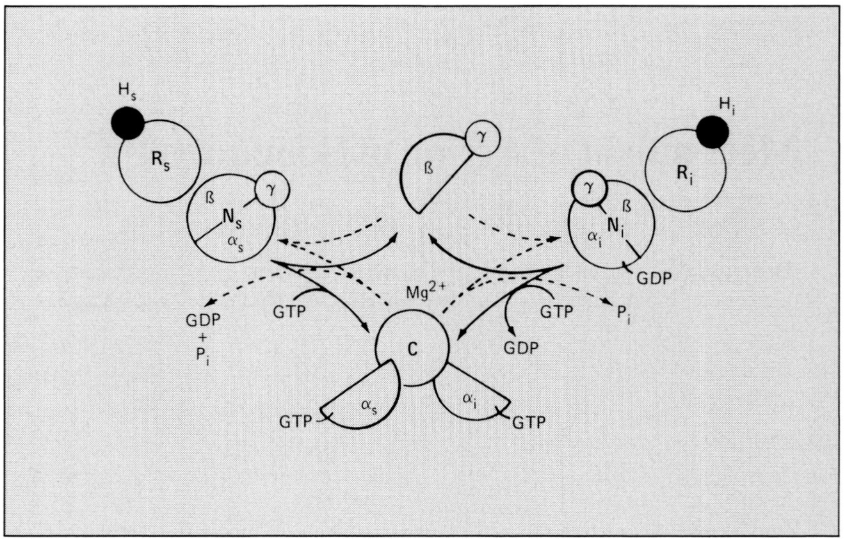

2

Fig. 1. Calmodulin content in different subcellular fractions of anterior pituitaries at different times of somatostatin (--○--) or TRH (—○—) injection to female rats.

Fig. 2. Multicomponent system of adenylyl cyclase. Hs (stimulatory hormones) or Hi (inhibitory hormones) interact with their corresponding receptors, Rs and Ri. In the presence of GTP, this interaction results in dissociation of the corresponding guanine-nucleotide-binding proteins, Ns and Ni, into a heterodimer and sGTP or iGTP, which interact with the catalytic component, C, leading, respectively, to its activation or inhibition.

(GTP), somatostatin inhibits forskolin-stimulated adenylyl cyclase with a parallel increase in the guanosine triphosphatase (GTPase) activity of the membranes. At the same time, Cronin et al. [10] showed that pretreatment with pertussis toxin could block the somatostatin-induced inhibition of GH release and cAMP accumulation from rat pituitary cells.

There is clear evidence that calcium ion movement also plays an important role in the action of somatostatin. In pituitary cells, somatostatin interferes with the response of GH or ACTH to high potassium or to calcium ionophores [11, 12]. Conflicting data, which may represent differences between cells, exist concerning blockade of the secretory response of different cell types by somatostatin and the mechanisms involved. Luini et al. [12] have reported that the increase in cytosolic calcium seen in AT-20 cells exposed to GRF, VIP, isoproterenol, forskolin and 8-Br-cAMP, is cAMP-mediated. In these experiments 8-Br-cAMP increased voltage-dependent calcium channels, and somatostatin blocked the increase in cytosolic calcium elicited by all secretagogues, except 8-Br-cAMP, which bypasses the cyclase.

The participation of an Ni-type component mediating the effects of somatostatin is well established. In AtT-20 tumor cells, pertussis toxin, which promotes ADP-ribosylation of the Ni component from NAD and inhibits the effects of this component, blocks the somatostatin inhibition on cyclic AMP accumulation stimulated by isoproterenol and forskolin [13]. Besides its effect on cyclase it has been demonstrated that Ni or an Ni-type component can also participate in the calcium-mobilizing biosignalling [14, 15]. Pretreatment of different cell types responsive to somatostatin with pertussis toxin blocks the somatostatin inhibition to different agents, including phorbol esters, 8-Br-cyclic AMP, TRH and VIP [16, 18]. Pertussis toxin pretreatment also blocks the somatostatin inhibition of calcium influx (measured with Quin-2), in response to high potassium [18]. These results clearly indicate that some of the effects of somatostatin, the inhibitory effects on the cyclase, on calcium channels opening and on phosphoinositide turnover, are transduced via the Ni component. Two different mechanisms for cyclase activation by Ni have been proposed. In both models, dissociation of Ni into its subunits (α

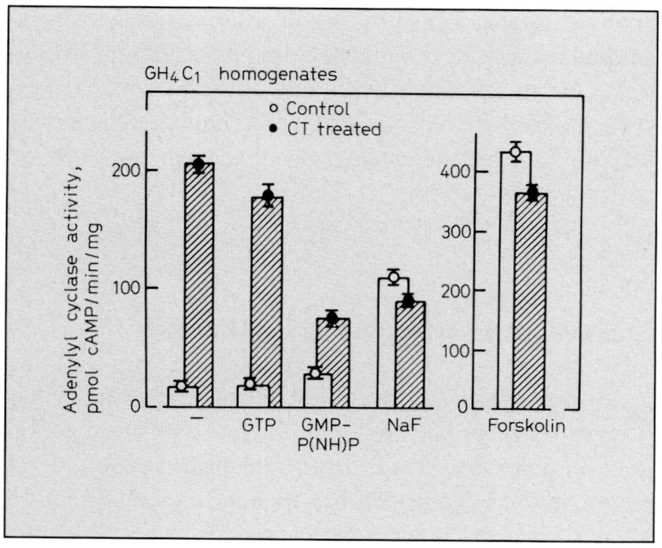

3

Fig. 3. Adenylyl cyclase activity of homogenates from GH4Cl cells nonpretreated (open bars) and pretreated with cholera toxin (dashed bars), analyzed in the presence GTP, GMPP(NH)P, NaF or forskolin. Data are expressed as means of triplicates ± SE.

Fig. 4. Adenylyl cyclase activity of homogenates from GH4Cl cells non pretreated (open circles) and pretreated with cholera toxin (closed circles), assayed in the presence or absence of VIP and increasing concentrations of somatostatin (SST).

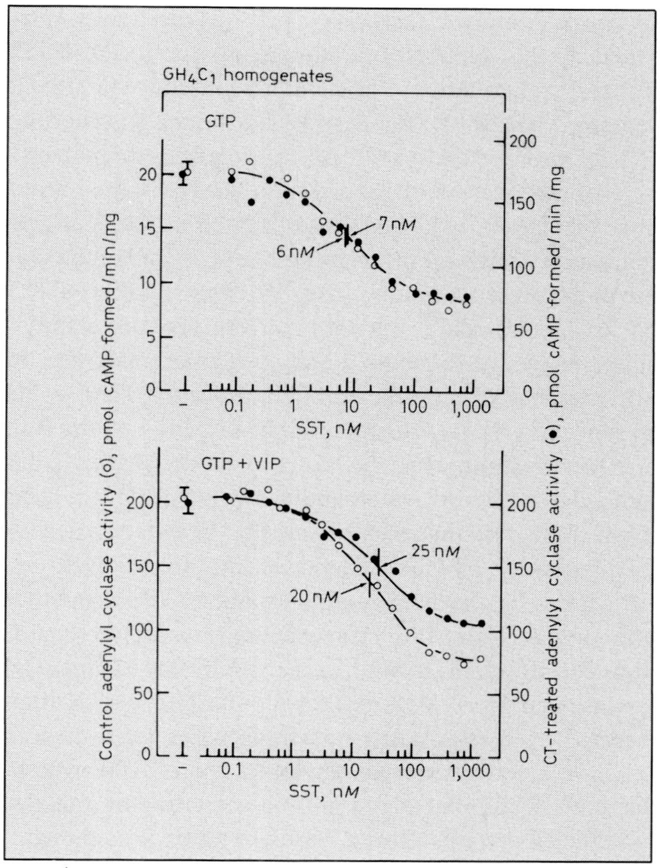

4

and βγ) is considered to be an essential step. In the first model, Ni activation would lead to subunit dissociation, therefore increasing the amount of free complex. By a mass-action effect, this would lead to association of the Ns complex, rendering it incapable of activating the cyclase. Secondly, direct interaction of αi with the catalytic component has also been postulated. There is experimental evidence supporting both models [19–22]. We have recently investigated both possibilities in GH4Cl cells, using somatostatin as the inhibitor [23] (fig. 3). Addition of GTP to homogenates from cholera toxin-treated cells resulted in a slight inhibition of the cyclase, and addition of 10 μ*M* GMP-P(NH)P or 10 m*M* NaF led to 60–70 or 40–50% inhibition of activity, respectively, reflecting the activation of the Ni pathway by these ligands [24]. Under the conditions of the assay (approximately 1 m*M* free Mg), the effects of stimulatory (VIP) and inhibitory (somatostatin) agents were studied in homogenates from control cells, the inhibitory effects being equally visible in the absence or presence of VIP (fig. 4). Treatment of cells with cholera toxin did not interfere with the inhibitory effect of somatostatin. How-

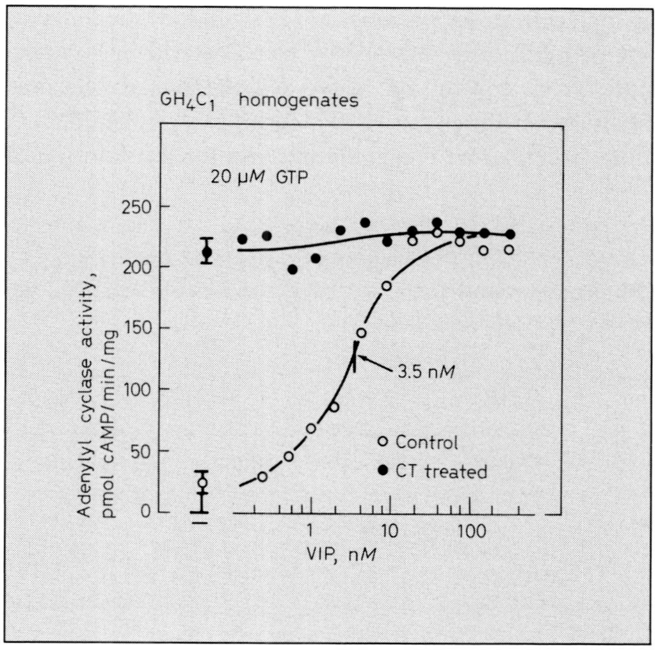

5

Fig. 5. Adenylyl cyclase activity of homogenates from GH4Cl cells non pretreated (open circles) and pretreated with cholera toxin (closed circles), assayed with increasing concentrations of VIP.

ever, the stimulatory action of VIP was essentially abolished by this agent (fig. 5), this being due to the GTP-dependent activation of the system caused by the toxin, leaving little room for further hormonal stimulation. These results clearly indicate that cholera toxin facilitates the activation of Ns and does not block the inhibitory regulation by hormones, estimated in terms of percentage of control. Furthermore, the IC_{50} for somatostatin in the presence or absence of VIP was variable (17–25 vs. 6–11 n*M*). Thus, a higher concentration of somatostatin is needed to obtain a half of the maximal effect in the presence of an Ns-stimulating hormone than in its absence (fig. 4). As illustrated in the same figure, the IC_{50} for somatostatin was the same in homogenates from both cholera toxin-treated and untreated cells. It is clear from these data that a treatment that both facilitates Ns activation by GTP and decreases the inhibition of this activation by the beta-gamma complex, affects neither the potency nor the efficiency with which receptor ligands stimulate Ni and cause inhibition of adenylyl cyclase activity. We think that the inhibitory regulation exerted by somatostatin in homogenates from cholera toxin-treated cells reflects the inhibition of ADP-ribosylated Ns/C complexes and not the regulation of traces of unaffected systems. Three reasons support this thought: (1) After 16 h of toxin treatment, no traces of Ns could be demonstrated; (2) VIP failed to further activate the cyclase activity in homogenates from cholera toxin-treated cells in the presence of GTP, and (3) the percentage of inhibition obtained by somatostatin in homogenates from control and cholera toxin-treated cells was unaltered in the presence of a stimulatory hormone. On these premises we conclude that hormonal inhibition of adenylyl cyclase is not the result of an increase of beta-gamma complexes originated from Ni activation. In contrast, and in agreement with data obtained with the cyc- system, Ni-mediated inhibition of adenylyl cyclase must actively involve the interaction of the adenylyl cyclase with the activated Ni.

Somatostatin Action on Cytosolic Enzymes

Modulation of phosphodiesterase (PDE) activity has been reported to participate in the mechanism of action of several hormones and neurotransmitters [25–27]. We have explored the possibility that besides its effect on adenylyl cyclase, somatostatin could also affect the anterior pituitary phosphodiesterase [28]. Most of the cytosolic enzyme is calmodulin-dependent and can be referred to both as cAMP PDE (high K_m) or cGMP PDE (low K_m) [29–31].

Normal female rats were injected with 20 µg of somatostatin/100 g body weight and sacrificed at 0, 5, 15 and 30 min after injection. cGMP PDE was assayed in the presence of EGTA with or without added calcium and calmodulin (CAM). Somatostatin did not affect PDE activity in the presence of EGTA, but an increase in the activity was seen when the enzyme was assayed in the presence of calcium or calcium-calmodulin (tables I and II). This increase was small, although significant at all times, due probably to the cellular heterogeneity of the preparation. The possibility of a covalent modification of the enzyme or interaction with an Ni-type protein is now under investigation.

Table I. Effect of somatostatin treatment on anterior pituitary phosphodiesterase activity, assayed in the presence of EGTA, calcium and calcium plus calmodulin

	Time			
	0 min	5 min	10 min	15 min
EGTA	4.84±0.28	4.92±0.21	5.46±0.18	4.86±0.19
Ca^{2+}	10.74±0.38	12.95±0.67*	13.67±0.26***	12.04±0.7
Ca^{2+}+CAM	10.63±0.43	12.66±0.69*	13.38±0.17***	11.94±0.76

Data (pmol of cGMP hydrolyzed/min/mg protein) are expressed as means ± SE of 5–7 samples. Asterisks indicate statistically significant differences vs. '0' time: * $p < 0.05$; ** $p < 0.01$; *** $p < 0.001$.

Table II. Effect of pretreatment with increasing amounts of somatostatin on phosphodiesterase activity in GH4C1 cell homogenates, assayed in the presence of EGTA, calcium and calcium plus calmodulin

	Somatostatin			
	0 µ*M*	0.01 µ*M*	0.1 µ*M*	1.0 µ*M*
EGTA	1.65	2.57	2.49	3.04
Ca^{2+}	2.00	4.01	5.16	5.65
Ca^{2+}+CAM	2.08	4.00	5.29	6.08

Data (pmol cGMP hydrolyzed/min/mg protein) are expressed as means of triplicates.

Conclusions

Somatostatin inhibits both basal and stimulated transduction systems at the membrane level by interacting with an Ri-type receptor coupled to an Ni component. This interaction results in inhibition of the adenylyl cyclase, calcium channels opening and probably phosphoinositide turnover. Besides these effects somatostatin is also able to stimulate soluble phosphodiesterase, therefore reinforcing its inhibitory effect on cyclase, by a mechanism not known at present.

Acknowledgements

We wish to thank Paloma Peers for editorial help. This work was supported by grants 1180 from the CACYT and from the Comitè Conjunto Hispano-Norteamericano para la Cooperacion Cientifica y Tecnologica.

References

1 Schombrunn, A.; Dorflinger, L.J.; Koch, B.D.: Mechanisms of somatostatin in pituitary cells; in Patel and Baum, Somatostatin. Advances in experimental medicine and biology, vol. 188, p. 305 (Plenum Press, New York 1985).

2 Draznin, B.; Sherman, N.; Sussman, K.; Dahl, R.; Vatter, A.: Internalization and cellular processing of somatostatin in primary culture of rat anterior pituitary cells. Endocrinology *117:* 960–966 (1985).

3 Conn, F.M.; Chafouleas, J.G.; Rogers, D.; Means, A.R.: Gonadotropin releasing hormone stimulates calmodulin redistribution in rat pituitary. Nature, Lond. *292:* 264–265 (1981).

4 Salisbury, J.L.; Condeelis, J.S.; Satir, P.: The role of coated vesicles, microfilaments and calmodulin in receptor-mediated endocytosis by cultured B lymphoblastoid cells. J. Cell Biol. *87:* 132–141 (1980).

5 Rodbell, M.: The role of hormone receptors and GTP-regulatory proteins in membrane transduction. Nature, Lond. *284:* 17–24 (1980).

6 Codina, J.; Hildebrandt, J.; Sunyer, T.; Sekura, R.D.; Manclark, C.R.; Iyengar, R.; Birnbaumer, L.: Mechanisms in the vectorial receptor-adenylate cyclase signal transduction. Adv. cycl. Nucleotides Phosphorylation Res. *17:* 111–125 (1984).

7 Gilman, A.: G proteins and dual control of adenylate cyclase. Cell *36:* 577–579 (1984).

8 Jacobs, K.H.; Aktories, K.; Schultz, G.: A nucleotide regulatory site for the somatostatin inhibition of adenylate cyclase in S49 lymphoma cells. Nature, Lond. *303:* 177–178 (1983).

9 Jacobs, K.H.; Schultz, G.: Occurrence of a hormone-sensitive inhibitory coupling component of the adenylate cyclase in S49 lymphoma cyc-variants. Proc. natn. Acad. Sci. USA *80:* 3899–3902 (1983).

10 Cronin, M.J.; Rogol, A.D.; Myers, G.A.; Hewlett, E.L.: Pertussis toxin blocks the somatostatin-induced inhibition of growth hormone release and adenosine 3′,5′-monophosphate accumulation. Endocrinology *113:* 209–215 (1983).

11 Richardson, U.I.: Adrenocorticotropin secretion by mouse pituitary tumor cells in culture: the role of Ca^{+2} in stimulated and somatostatin-inhibited secretion. Endocrinology *113:* 62–68 (1983).

12 Luini, A.; Lewis, D.; Guild, B.; Corda, D.; Axelrod, J.: Hormone secretagogues increase cytosolic calcium by increasing cAMP in corticotropin-secreting cells. Proc. natn. Acad. Sci. USA *82:* 8034–8038 (1985).

13 Reisine, T.D.; Zhang, Y.; Sekura, R.D.: Pertussis toxin blocks somatostatin inhibition of stimulated cyclic AMP accumulation in anterior pituitary tumor cells. Biochem. biophys. Res. Commun. *115:* 794–799 (1983).

14 Okajima, F.; Ui, M.: ADP-ribosilation of the specific membrane protein islet-activating proteins, pertussis toxin, associated with inhibitions of a chemotactic peptide-induced arachidonate release in neutrophils. A possible role of the toxin substrate in Ca^{2+}-mobilizing biosignaling. J. biol. Chem. *259:* 13863–13871 (1984).

15 Ohta, H.: Okajima, F.; Ui, M.: Inhibition by islet-activating protein of a chemotactic peptide-induced early breakdown of inositol phospholipids and Ca^{2+} mobilization in guinea pig neutrophils. J. biol. Chem. *260:* 15771–15780 (1985).

16 Heisler, S.: The inhibitory guanine nucleotide-binding regulatory subunit of adenylate cyclase has an adenylate cyclase-independent modulatory effect on ACTH secretion from pure pituitary tumor cells. Biochem. biophys. Res. Commun. *126:* 941–947 (1985).

17 Yajima, Y.; Akita, Y.; Saito, T.: Pertussis toxin blocks the inhibitory effects of somatostatin on cAMP-dependent vasoactive intestinal peptide and cAMP-independent thyrotropin releasing hormone-stimulated prolactin secretion in GH3 cells. J. biol. Chem. *261:* 2684–2689 (1986).

18 Koch, B.D.; Dorflinger, L.J.; Schonbrunn, A.: Pertussis toxin blocks both cyclic AMP-mediated and cyclic AMP-independent actions of somatostatin. Evidence for coupling of Ni to decreases in intracellular free calcium. J. biol. Chem. *260:* 13138–13145 (1985).

19 Birnbaumer, L.; Codina, J.; Mattera, R.; Cerione, R.A.; Hildebrandt, J.D.; Sunyer, T.; Rojas, F.J.; Caron, M.G.; Lefkowitz, R.J.; Iyengar, R.: Structural basis of adenylate cyclase stimulation and inhibition by distinct guanine nucleotide regulatory proteins; in Cohen, Houslay, Molecular mechanisms of transmembrane signaling, p. 131 (Elsevier, Amsterdam 1985).

20 Katada, T.; Bokoch, G.M.; Nortrup, J.K.; Ui, M.; Gilman, A.G.: The inhibitory guanine nucleotide-binding regulatory component of adenylate cyclase. Properties and function of the purified protein. J. biol. Chem. *259:* 3568–3577 (1984).

21 Katada, T.; Bokoch, G.M.; Smigel, M.D.; Ui, M.; Gilman, A.G.: The inhibitory guanine nucleotide-binding regulatory component of adenylate cyclase. Subunit dissociation and the inhibition of adenylate cyclase in S49 lymphoma cyc- and wild type membranes. J. biol. Chem. *259:* 3586–3595 (1984).

22 Cerione, R.A.; Staniszewski, C.; Gierschik, P.; Codina, J.; Somers, R.L.; Birnbaumer, L.; Spiegel, A.M.; Caron, M.G.; Lefkowitz, R.L.: Mechanisms of guanine nucleotide regulatory protein-mediated inhibition of adenylate cyclase. J. biol. Chem. *261:* 9514–9520 (1986).

23 Toro, M.J.; Montoya, E.; Birnbaumer, L.: Inhibitory regulation of adenylyl cyclase. Evidence inconsistent with β-γ complexes of Gi protein mediating hormonal effects interfering

with activation of GS. Mol. Endocrinol. *1:* 669–676 (1987).
24 Hildebrandt, J.D.; Birnbaumer, L.: Inhibitory regulation of adenylyl cyclase in the absence of stimulatory regulation. Requirements and kinetics of guanine nucleotide-induced inhibition of the cyc-S49 adenylyl cyclase. J. biol. Chem. *258:* 13141–13147 (1983).
25 Loten, E.G.; Sneyd, J.G.T.: An effect of insulin on adipose tissue adenoside 3′5′-monophosphate phosphodiesterase. Biochem. J. *120:* 187–193 (1970).
26 Barber, R.; Ray, K.P.; Butcher, R.W.: Turnover of adenosine 3′5′-monophosphate in WI-38 cultured fibroblasts. Biochemistry *19:* 2560–2567 (1980).
27 Dumont, J.E.; Takeuchi, A.; Lamy, F.; Gervy-Decoster, C.; Cochaux, P.; Roger, P.; Van Sande, J.; Lecoq, R.; Mochel, J.: Thyroid control. An example of a complex cell regulation network. Adv. cycl. Nucleotides Phosphorylation Res. *14:* 479–489 (1981).
28 Redon, M.C.; Toro, M.J.; Montoya, E.: Somatostatin stimulates phosphodiesterase in rat anterior pituitary and brain. Adv. cycl. Nucleotides Phosphorylation Res. (in press).
29 Appleman, M.M.; Airano, M.A.; Takemoto, D.J.; Whitson, R.H.: Cyclic nucleotide phosphodiesterase; in Nathanson, Kebabian, Handbook of experimental pharmacology, vol. 58/1, p. 263 (Springer, Berlin 1982).
30 Cheung, W.Y.; Storm, R.D.: Calmodulin regulation of cyclic AMP metabolism; in Nathanson, Kebabian, Handbook of experimental pharmacology, vol. 58/1, p. 300 (Springer, Berlin 1982).
31 Azhar, S.; Menon, K.M.J.: Cyclic nucleotide phosphodiesterase from rat anterior pituitary. Characterization by protein activator and Ca^{2+}. Eur. J. Biochem. *73:* 73–82 (1977).

Dr. E. Montoya
Departamento de Bioquimica
Facultad de Medicina
Alcala de Henares (Spain)

Hormone Res. *29:* 65–69 (1988)

Somatostatin Receptors in Normal and Tumoral Tissue

J.C. Reubi [a], *S.W.J. Lamberts* [b], *R. Maurer* [a]

[a] Sandoz Research Institute, Berne, Switzerland; [b] Department of Medicine, Erasmus University, Rotterdam, Holland

Key Words. Somatostatin receptors · Tumors · Incidence · Tissue localization

Abstract. Somatostatin receptors have been visualized with autoradiography and characterised biochemically in various somatostatin target tissues, such as brain, pituitary, pancreas and gastrointestinal tract, where they are likely to mediate the somatostatin actions. With the same methods, somatostatin receptors have been detected also in tumors originating from somatostatin target tissues: high receptor incidence is found in GH-producing pituitary adenomas as well as in some hormone-producing gastrointestinal tumors. These tumors are often highly responsive to somatostatin analogs in vivo. Among brain tumors, meningiomas usually contain a high density of receptors, suggesting a novel function for somatostatin in the human meninges. Among other human tumors tested, prostate, ovarian and endometrial carcinomas were free of receptors whereas 3 out of 39 mammary tumors contained somatostatin receptors.

Introduction

In the past few years, there has been increasing evidence that the action of somatostatin (SS), consisting mainly of the inhibition of hormone release in a large number of tissues, is mediated through specific SS receptors located in these tissues. In this report, we will first briefly review the current data on the distribution of SS receptors in nonpathological tissues in the laboratory rat and in man. Secondly, we will present our recent data on the distribution of SS receptors in various endocrine and nonendocrine human tumors.

SS Receptors in Normal Tissues

SS receptors have been shown to be present in all the main sites of action of SS in the rat, such as the pituitary, the endocrine and exocrine pancreas, the gastrointestinal tract, the adrenals and the CNS. Moreover, in some cases, normal human postmortem material has been studied. SS receptors were either measured with biochemical techniques, i.e. binding on homogenate in vitro, or visualized with autoradiography. Various radioligands, all specific for SS receptors, have been used, such as SS-14 analogs, SS-28 analogs or analogs of the stable SS octapeptide SMS 201-995.

In all tissues, high affinity and saturable binding sites with pharmacological specificity for biologically active SS analogs were identified [1–3]. Interestingly, the affinity of the receptor for certain SS analogs may differ from tissue to tissue, suggesting that the SS receptors in these various tissues may be heterogeneous to some extent.

Within the rat CNS, there is a topographically very precise distribution of the SS receptors. They are mainly located in cortical areas and the limbic system, such as the hippocampus, the amygdala and the septum (fig. 1A). Also some primary sensory afferents such as the substantia gelatinosa of the spinal cord contain significant amounts of receptors. The majority of SS receptors seem to be localised on neurons, which is compatible with a neurotransmitter role of SS. Thanks to the good postmortem stability of these receptors, they could be detected in human brain in most of the above-mentioned sites such as cortex, hippocampus or amygdala. High densities of receptors are found in the basal ganglia and, unexpectedly, in the human cerebellum as well.

In the pituitary gland of the rat, SS receptors are located in the anterior part, in particular on somatotrophs but also on thyreotrophs and lactotrophs, where they mediate inhibition of hormone release (fig. 1C). The human pituitary gland has also been shown to contain SS receptors.

Both the endocrine and exocrine pancreas bear specific SS receptors. Within the islets, the B, A and D cells all possess such receptors, compatible with the inhibitory action of SS on insulin or glucagon. In the exocrine part of the rat pancreas, the acinar cells have SS receptors which could be partially characterized biochemically as high molecular weight proteins.

In the gastrointestinal tract, SS receptors are difficult to identify on cell membranes. However, they have been identified in the rat stomach mucosa within the cytosol fraction of the cell. Although they are expected to mediate SS inhibition of various gastrointestinal hormones, the precise role of such intracellular SS receptors is not yet fully established.

Finally, the rat adrenal has SS receptors in the zona glomerulosa which mediate inhibition of the angiotensin-stimulated aldosterone release; interestingly, the rat medulla also seem to possess SS receptors (fig. 1B). But is should be noticed that a strong species-specificity for SS receptors exist in the adrenal: some species have only medullary receptors, others only glomerulosa receptors; others, such as humans, have no adrenal SS receptors at all [2].

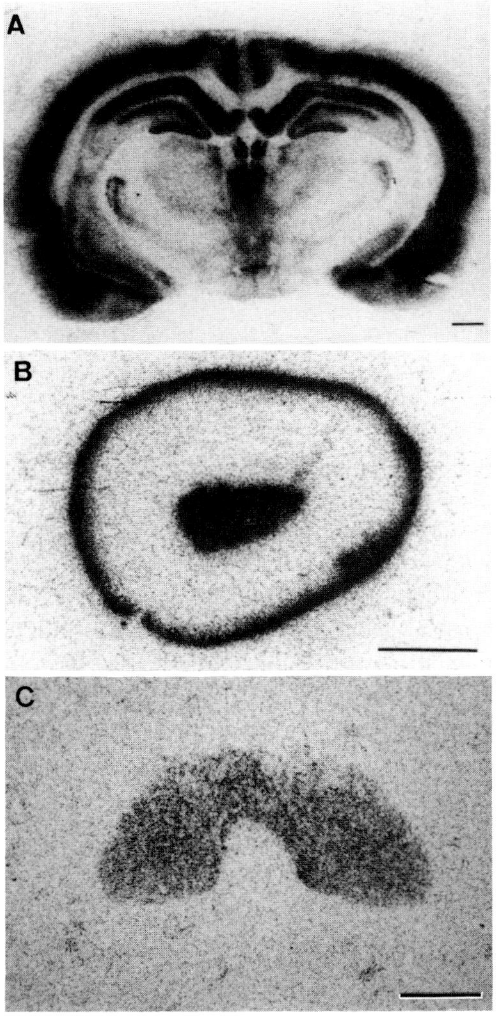

Fig. 1. Somatostatin receptors in 3 different rat tissues. **A** Coronal section of the brain. **B** Adrenal gland. **C** Pituitary. Photos of autoradiograms on [^{3}H]LKB Ultrofilm are shown. **A** and **B** represent in vitro incubation with ^{125}I-204-090, whereas C is the result of in vivo labelling with ^{125}I-204-090. Bar = 1 mm.

SS Receptors in Human Tumoral Tissue

Interest for the study of tumors in relation to SS stems not only from the general inhibitory action of SS on growth through inhibition of GH, somatomedin and insulin. SS seems to have antiproliferative action on certain tissues stimulated by growth factors, but not on the basal mechanism of cell division. Moreover, chronic application of the SS analog SMS 201-995 inhibits the growth of some transplantable animal tumors and leads to shrinkage of some types of human tumors as well. Part of these actions are likely to be mediated by SS receptors [4, 5] located on the tumor itself.

Pituitary Tumors

The presence of SS receptors in all acromegalic adenomas tested (fig. 2A, B) confirms previous studies with cell cultures and clinical tests on the efficacy of SS in this disease. Interestingly, two types of acromegalic adenomas seem to exist, those with high density of SS receptors, and those with low amounts of nonhomogeneously distributed SS receptors [6–8]. It may be speculated that these types correspond to the two clinical subgroups of SS-responsive and SS-nonresponsive acromegalics. Prolactinomas, usually bromocriptine treated, have only low levels or no SS receptors. Interestingly, endocrine inactive pituitary adenomas also possess in a significant number of cases specific SS receptors, despite the absence of immunoreactive GH in the tissue.

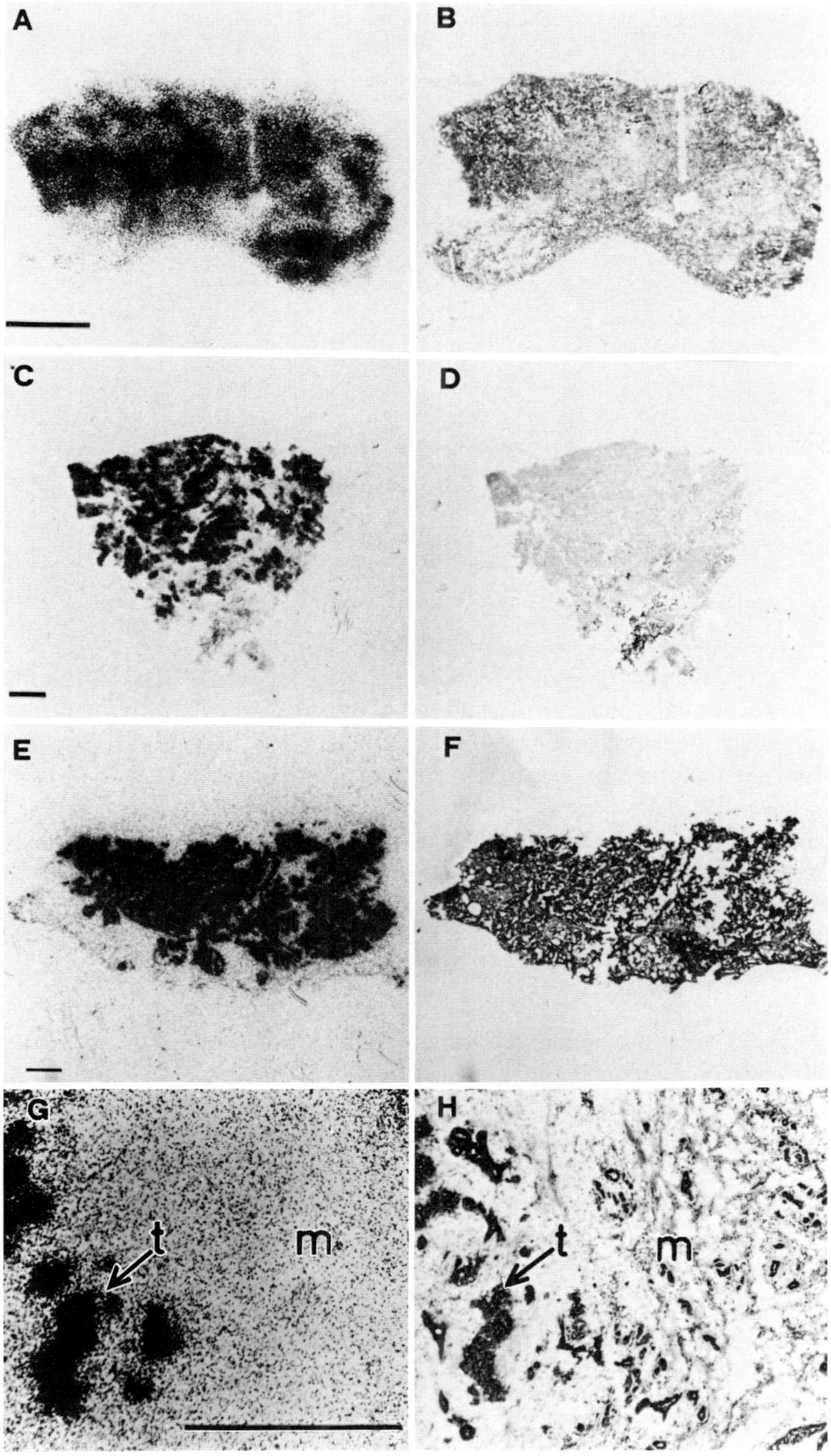

Fig. 2. Distribution of SS receptors in various types of human tumors. **A**, **B** Autoradiogram (total binding) and respective tissue section from a GH-producing pituitary adenoma. **C**, **D** Autoradiogram and respective tissue section from a meningioma. **E**, **F** Autoradiogram and respective tissue section from a GRF-producing gut carcinoma. **G**, **H** Autoradiogram and respective tissue section from a mammary tumor. t = Tumor cell clusters showing high density of SS receptors; m = normal mammary gland tissue without SS receptors. In all cases, nonspecific binding was negligible. Time of exposure was 1 week. Bars = 1 mm.

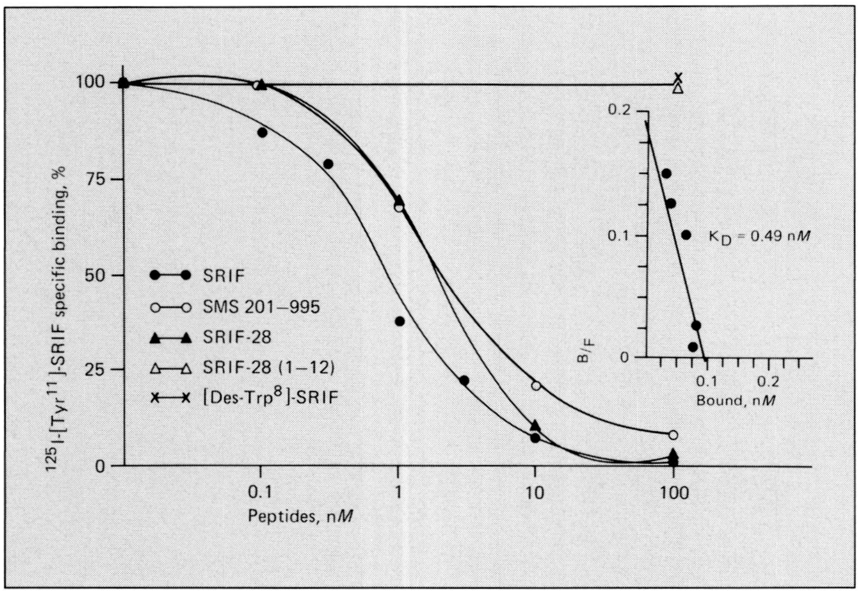

Fig. 3. Somatostatin receptors in human meningiomas. Binding of ^{125}I-[Tyr^{11}]-SS to human meningioma membranes. Displacement of radioligand by increasing concentrations of SS, SMS 201-995, SS-28, SS-28(1-12) and Des-Trp^{8}-SS. The points represent the average of triplicate tubes. Insert: Scatchard plot of the inhibition curve with SS, K_D = 0.49 n*M*, B_{max} = 294 fmol/mg protein. P_2 membranes were incubated for 30 min at 22 °C with 40,000 cpm radioligand. Total binding was 19.7% of which 7% was not displaced by 100 n*M* SS.

Brain Tumors

Unexpectedly, one type of brain tumor, the meningioma, which does not originate from neurons or glia but from the leptomeninx, has a very high incidence of SS receptors [9]. They are only localized over tumoral tissue (fig. 2C, D) and have all the biochemical characteristics of true SS receptors (fig. 3). Since normal human leptomeninx bear SS receptors, a physiological role for SS in this tissue may be postulated.

Gut Tumors

Three GRF-producing gut tumors were tested and shown to contain large amounts of specific SS receptors [3] over the tumor tissue (fig. 2E, F). Since these tumors are responsive in vivo to chronic SMS 201-995 treatment in the form of an inhibition of GRF release as well as by shrinkage, it is likely that the SS receptors situated on these tumors are mediators of these in vivo effects.

Other Tumors

All tested prostate, endometrial and ovarian tumors were SS receptor-negative. Aldosteronomas and pheochromocytomas were also negative, which may be explained by the lack of SS receptors in human adrenals. From 39 mammary tumors tested, 3 had significant amounts of SS receptors [3]. Those were restricted to the tumoral tissue (fig. 2G, H). Since adjacent healthy mammary gland tissue was lacking such SS receptors, this suggests that SS receptors are newly expressed in these tumors as a consequence of tumorous transformation. The low number of SS receptor-positive cases may represent a subclass of mammary tumors, possibly responsive to therapy with SS analogs.

Conclusions

SS receptors are present in tumors originating from established SS target tissues, such as acromegalic adenomas. Such receptors are, however, also present in tumors originating from tissues without previously established links to SS, such as meningiomas or mammary tumors. In some of the tumors, i.e. the gut GRFomas, a good correlation between the presence of SS receptors and the in vivo responsiveness to SS analogs can be found. This may point towards the usefulness of SS receptor measurements in tumors in order to predict new therapeutical applications for SS analogs. This may be particularly interesting for tumors without previously established links to SS, such as meningiomas, in case an inhibitory role of SS on peptide release or cell division can indeed be found in these tissues.

References

1 Reubi, J.C.; Cortes, R.; Maurer, R.; Probst, A.; Palacios, J.M.: Distribution of somatostatin receptors in the human brain. An autoradiographic study. Neuroscience *18:* 329–346 (1986).
2 Maurer, R.; Reubi, J.C.: Somatostatin receptors in the adrenal. Mol. cell. Endocrinol. *45:* 81–90 (1986).

3 Reubi, J.C.; Maurer, R.; Werder, K. von; Torhorst, J.; Klijn, J.G.M.; Lamberts, S.W.J.: Somatostatin receptors in human endocrine tumors. Cancer Res. *47:* 551–558 (1987).
4 Reubi, J.C.: A somatostatin analogue inhibits chondrosarcoma and insulinoma tumor growth. Acta endocr., Copenh. *109:* 108–114 (1985).
5 Lamberts, S.W.J.; Reubi, J.C.; Uitterlinden, P.; Zuiderwijk, J.; Werff, P. van den; Hal, P.: Studies on the mechanism of action of the inhibitory effect of the somatostatin analog SMS 201–995 on the growth of the PRL/ACTH secreting pituitary tumor 7315a. Endocrinology *118:* 2188–2194 (1986).
6 Reubi, J.C.; Landolt, A.M.: High density of somatostatin receptors in pituitary tumors from acromegalic patients. J. clin. Endocr. Metab. *59:* 1148–1151 (1984).
7 Moyse, E.; Le Dafniet, M.; Epelbaum, J.; Pagesy, P.; Peillon, F.; Kordon, C.; Enjalbert, A.: Somatostatin receptors in human growth hormone and prolactin-secreting pituitary adenomas. J. clin. Endocr. Metab. *61:* 98–103 (1985).
8 Ikuyama, S.; Nawata, H.; Kato, K.; Karshima, T.; Ibayashi, H.; Nakagaki, H.: Specific somatostatin receptors on human pituitary adenoma cell membranes. J. clin. Endocr. Metab. *61:* 666–671 (1985).
9 Reubi, J.C.; Maurer, R.; Klijn, J.G.M.; Stefanko, S.Z.; Foekens, J.A.; Blaauw, G.; Blankenstein, M.A.; Lamberts, S.W.J.: High incidence of somatostatin receptors in human meningiomas. Biochemical characterization. J. clin. Endocr. Metab. *63:* 433–438 (1986).

J.C. Reubi
Sandoz Research Institute
PO Box 2173
CH–3001 Berne (Switzerland)

Hormone Res. *29:* 70–74 (1988)

0301–0163/88/0293–0070$2.75/0

Somatostatin as a Physiological Regulator of Pulsatile Growth Hormone Secretion

Gloria Shaffer Tannenbaum

Neuropeptide Physiology Laboratory, McGill University-Montreal Children's Hospital Research Institute, and the Departments of Pediatrics, Neurology and Neurosurgery, McGill University, Montreal, P.Q., Canada

Key Words. Growth hormone · Somatostatin · Growth hormone-releasing factor · Passive immunization · Hypothalamus · Rhythm · Nutritional status · Feedback regulation

Abstract. Somatostatin plays an important role in the regulation of the episodic and ultradian rhythm of growth hormone (GH) secretion. Passive immunization of rats with specific antibodies to the 14 and 28 amino acid sequences caused a significant GH elevation. The fact that somatostatin antiserum was unable to block episodic GH surges indicates that this hormone's release must be regulated by a dual mechanism. Indeed, GH-releasing factor (GRF) seems to be instrumental in the maintenance of pulsatile GH secretion. Moreover, exogenous GRF induced a further GH increase predominantly during the period of active secretion. Neutralization of endogenous somatostatin eliminated this time-dependent effect, indicating that this peptide blocks periodical spontaneous GH release. Food deprivation and changes in glucose homeostasis virtually obliterate the ultradian GH rhythm. In this context, peripheral somatostatin seems to play an important role. Also the central GRF/somatostatin interplay is responsible for a short-loop feedback control on pituitary somatotrops.

Introduction

Growth hormone (GH) is secreted episodically in all species, including man. Current knowledge indicates that the pulsatile pattern of GH release from the pituitary gland is the net result of a delicate interplay between two hypothalamic hormones, a stimulatory, GH-releasing factor (GRF), and a GH release-inhibiting hormone, somatostatin. This brief review will focus on the importance of somatostatin as a physiological regulator of pulsatile GH secretion.

Somatostatin as a Physiological Regulator of the Normal Ultradian Rhythm of GH Secretion

In every mammalian species studied so far, spontaneous episodes of GH secretion occur several times over a 24-hour period. Particularly in the rat, GH release follows a striking ultradian rhythm with high-amplitude GH secretory bursts occurring at regular 3.3-hour intervals [1]. In the intervening trough periods, basal plasma GH levels are undetectable (fig. 1A).

The cyclic tetradecapeptide, somatostatin, which was originally isolated from the hypothalamus as a GH inhibitory factor, has subsequently been shown to exert profound inhibitory effects on GH release in response to virtually all known stimuli. Following the isolation and characterization of a larger molecular weight form of somatostatin, somatostatin-28, we demonstrated that this peptide exhibited potent inhibitory activity on spontaneous GH release which persisted for a significantly longer period of time than that of somatostatin-14 [2]. These findings suggested that somatostatin-28 may not merely be a prohormone, but may act as a regulatory hormone on its own to influence GH secretion.

To determine the role of the endogenous somatostatin peptides in generation of the normal ultradian rhythm of GH secretion, we used the technique of passive immunization. The antiserum used was highly specific for somatostatin and detects both somatostatin-14 and somatostatin-28 with equal affinity. As illustrated in figure 1B, the i.v. administration of somatostatin antiserum to unanesthetized, freely-moving rats caused a significant elevation of GH trough levels. A similar augmentation of baseline GH levels following immunoneutralization with anti-somatostatin serum has been documented in several other species. These results suggested that endogenous circulating somatostatin is a physiologic regulator of GH trough periods and is likely released episodically into the hypophyseal portal circulation to inhibit pituitary GH release. Moreover, since the episodic bursts of GH release were not abolished by neutralization with somatostatin antiserum (fig. 1B), the findings provided support for the view that GH secretio must be regulated by the interaction of at least two hypothalamic hormones, one inhibitory, somatostatin, and the other excitatory, GRF.

The recent discovery of the GRF peptides provided a valuable tool to further delineate the physiological role of somatostatin, and its interrelationship with GRF, in regulation of pulsatile GH secretion. We first demonstrated that GRF was a powerful releaser of GH in GH-deficient animals bearing lesions of the ventromedial-arcuate (VMN-ARC) region of the hypothalamus, the neural locus shown by immunocytochemistry to harbor the GRF neurons [3]. These findings suggested that the ultradian surges of GH release are likely dependent on the episodic release of GRF from this region of the brain. We then studied the interaction of somatostatin and GRF in vivo by administering somatostatin-14 simultaneously with GRF to VMN-ARC lesioned rats. The concomitant administration of the two peptides markedly inhibited GRF's ability to release GH [3], indicating that somatostatin can antagonize the actions of GRF. This observation, together with those of in vitro studies demonstrating that somatostatin inhibits GRF-induced GH release from dispersed rat pituitary cells in typical noncompetitive antagonism, supported the view that somatostatin and GRF have different receptors on the pituitary somatotrophes.

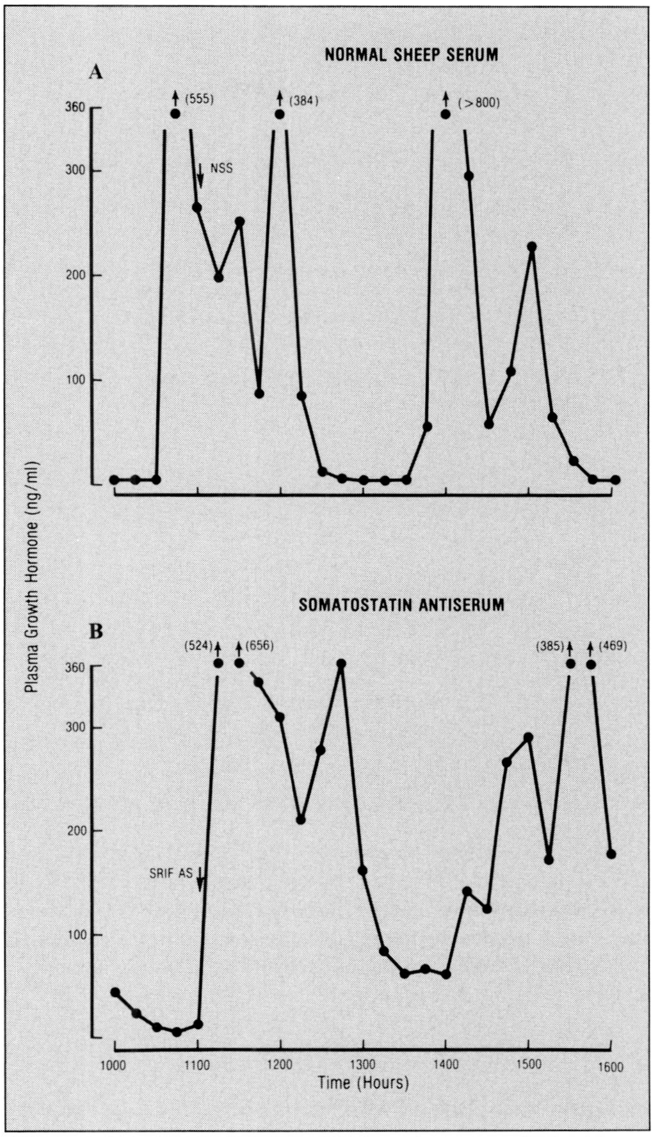

Fig. 1. Effect of passive immunization with somatostatin antiserum on spontaneous GH secretory profile. **A** The typical ultradian rhythm of GH secretion is evident in normal sheep serum-treated rats. **B** Administration of anti-somatostatin serum caused a significant elevation of GH through levels.

We continued to utilize the GRF peptides as probes to elucidate the interrelationship of somatostatin and GRF in generation of the ultradian GH rhythm in normal animals [4]. By administering GRF during both peak and trough periods of the rhythm, we showed a striking time-dependent difference in the magnitude of the GH response to GRF; injection of GRF during a time of peak GH secretion resulted in a 2- to 3-fold increase in plasma GH, whereas injection during a trough period had only a minimal effect (fig. 2). Neutralization of endogenous circulating somatostatin eliminated the time-dependent difference, indicating that the weak GRF-induced GH release observed during trough times is due to antagonization by endogenous somatostatin. Thus, these data provided further support for the hypothesis that the release of somatostatin from the hypothalamus into the hypophyseal portal blood is increased episodically during trough periods. Somatostatin

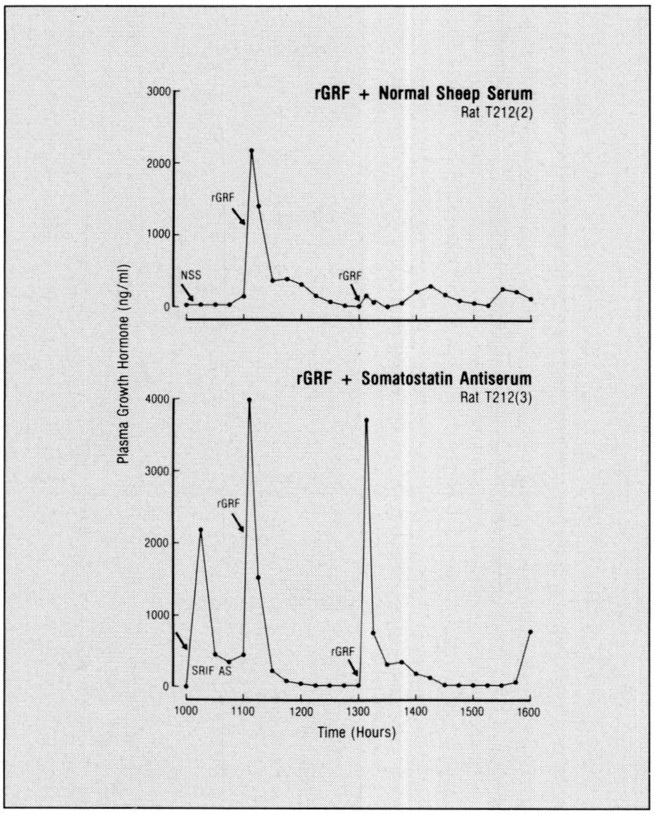

Fig. 2. GH responsiveness to rGRF administered during peak and trough periods of the GH rhythm. The plasm GH response to rGRF was significantly greater during a time of peak GH secretion than during a trough period in normal sheep serum-treated animals (upper panel). Passive immunization with somatostatin antiserum reserved this time-dependent difference (lower panel).

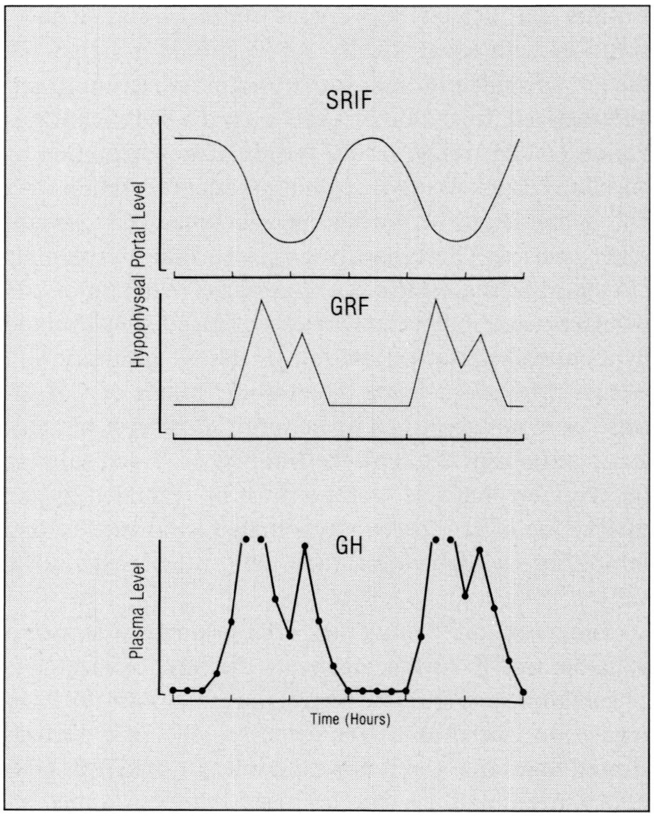

Fig. 3. Postulated rhythmic secretion of hypothalamic somatostatin (SRIF) and GRF into hypophyseal portal blood, with the net result on pituitary GH secretion as observed in plasma. From Tannenbaum and Ling [4], with permission.

secretion also appears to continue at a low basal rate to inhibit GH secretion during peak periods, since immunoneutralization with anti-somatostatin serum further augmented the GH response to GRF during peak GH secretion (fig. 2).

These results, together with the available evidence to date, led us to propose the hypothesis shown schematically in figure 3 that somatostatin is secreted tonically from the hypothalamus into the hypophyseal portal blood, and that superimposed upon this steady state release is an additional rhythmic surge with a periodicity of 3–4 h. A similar pattern of GRF secretion, approximately 180 minutes out of phase with somatostatin secretion, is responsible for generating the ultradian rhythm of GH secretion as observed in the peripheral blood. Recent experiments by Plotsky and Vale [5] in which they directly measured levels of immunoreactive somatostatin and GRF in rat hypophyseal portal blood, are strongly supportive of this hypothesis. Moreover, studies by Vance et al. [6] also offer support to the concept that intermittent surges of somatostatin secretion may account for the GH trough levels in man, since the intrinsic pulsatile pattern of GH secretion was preserved during constant infusion with GRF. Their elegant findings complement those in the rat and suggest that the pulses of GH secretion in man are likely regulated by a combination of enhanced GRF secretion with concomitant reduction of somatostatin secretion.

Somatostatin as a Mediator of Disorders of GH Secretion

The neuroendocrine mechanisms regulating GH secretion appear to be exquisitively sensitive and responsive to nutritional status. We have demonstrated that the normal ultradian GH rhythm is virtually obliterated in response to food deprivation, insulinopenic diabetes, and intracellular glucopenia [7]. Passive immunization with anti-somatostatin serum restored high-amplitude GH secretory bursts in both starved and diabetic rats, which suggests that circulating somatostatin plays a physiological role in mediating the GH suppression observed in these conditions.

The increased somatostatin reaching the pituitary under these conditions could originate from the hypothalamus or from peripheral tissues. The latter is more likely since marked alterations in pancreatic, gastrointestinal and blood, but not hypothalamic, concentrations of somatostatin have been documented in starvation and various forms of diabetes. Additional evidence implicating peripherally produced somatostatin comes from recent studies in which we observed a significant elevation of plasma somatostatin-like immunoreactive levels in rats subjected to prolonged food deprivation, but no difference in in vitro basal and K^+-stimulated somatostatin release from incubated hypothalamic fragments [8]. Interestingly, the results of this work suggest that the pattern of somatostatin secretion during starvation is converted to a tonic, rather than episodic, mode of release which likely explains the prolonged suppression of GH secretion observed in this situation. All these findings are compatible with the hypothesis that somatostatin may be an important hormonal regulator of nutrient homeostasis, and suggest that somatostatin originating from peripheral sites can exert an endocrine-like action on a distant target organ such as the pituitary gland to alter GH secretion.

Somatostatin antiserum also reverses, at least partially, the GH-inhibitory reactions to stress, implicating somatostatin as a physiological regulator of the GH suppression response to stressful stimuli.

Role of Somatostatin in Feedback Regulation of GH Secretion

There is now considerable evidence to suggest that GH is capable of regulating its own secretion through a shortloop negative feedback system at the level of the brain. We demonstrated that administration of rat GH into the lateral cerebral ventricle causes a severe suppression in amplitude of spontaneous GH pulses and similar findings have been reported using human GH. Hypothalamic somatostatin seems to play a role in GH autoregulation. Somatostatin concentrations in the hypothalamus are markedly altered in response to perturbations in GH levels. Furthermore, in vitro administration of GH results in a dose-dependent increase in somatostatin release from incubated rat hypothalami, and intraventricularly administered rGH provokes a dose-related increase in somatostatin release into the hypophyseal portal blood. To assess the physiological significance of the GH-induced somatostatin release on GH secretion, we examined the effects of passive immunization with somatostatin antiserum in rats given rGH centrally. The results provided support for only a partial role for somatostatin as a physiological mediator of GH autofeedback since anti-somatostatin failed to normalize GH pulse amplitude. Only a combination of anti-somatostatin serum and GRF administered intravenously permitted complete restoration of high-amplitude GH secretory bursts in such rats [9]. These results support the view that the mechanism whereby GH inhibits its own secretion likely involves decreased output of hypothalamic GRF concomitant with increased somatostatin release.

We also assessed the involvement of the somatomedin/insulin-like growth factors (IGFs) in feedback regulation of pulsatile GH secretion. Intracerebroventricular administration of a preparation enriched in IGFs suppressed spontaneous GH secretory pulses, suggesting that the somatomedin/IGFs may participate in a long-loop GH-negative feedback system [10]. Evidence for a role for somatostatin in mediating this response comes from studies by Berelowitz et al. [11] which demonstrate that somatomedin directly stimulates somatostatin release from rat hypothalamic fragments in vitro. Thus, somatomedin/IGFs may inhibit GH secretion by increasing the release of somatostatin, although the possibility that the somatomedins exert a simultaneous inhibitory action on hypothalamic GRF release remains to be explored.

Finally, evidence is accumulating to suggest that somatostatin may be capable of regulating its own secretion. Lumpkin et al. [12] demonstrated that central injection of somatostatin caused a paradoxical release of GH and postulated that hypothalamic somatostatin may self-regulate. Analogs of somatostatin that are biologically active, but inactive immunologically, have been shown to inhibit somatostatin secretion in vitro from cultured fetal hypothalamic cells [13]. These observations suggest that an ultrashort loop feedback mechanism may exist within the hypothalamus for autoregulation of somatostatinergic neurons. In addition, recent immunohistochemical studies have revealed possible synaptic interactions between somatostatin and GRF neurons, and GRF has been shown to directly stimulate somatostatin release from hypothalamic and median eminence fragments. Taken together, these latter findings suggest the possibility of reciprocal regulation between GRF and somatostatin neurons.

Conclusion

While it is apparent that we are only beginning to understand the complex physiological control mechanisms that govern the rhythmic secretion of GH, it is clear that the ubiquitous peptide, somatostatin, is at the very centre of things. Moreover, it is likely that disruption of its normal actions contributes to the pathogenesis of disorders of GH secretion. Significant advances have been made recently. The challenge to future research remains to further our knowledge of the physiological contributions of somatostatin to the intricate pathways of GH regulation.

Acknowledgements

This work was supported by grants from the Medical Research Council of Canada. The author is a Senior Scholar of the Fonds de la recherche en santé du Québec. The technical assistance of Wendy Gurd and Martine Lapointe, and the secretarial assistance of Julie Temko are gratefully acknowledged.

References

1 Tannenbaum, G.S.; Martin, J.B.: Evidence for an endogenous ultradian rhythm governing growth hormone secretion in the rat. Endocrinology *98:* 562–570 (1976).

2 Tannenbaum, G.S.; Ling, N.; Brazeau, P.: Somatostatin-28 is longer acting and more selective than somatostatin-14 on pituitary and pancreatic hormone release. Endocrinology *111:* 101–107 (1982).

3 Tannenbaum, G.S.; Eikelboom, R.; Ling, N.: Human pancreas GH-releasing factor analog restores high-amplitude GH pulses in CNS lesion-induced GH deficiency. Endocrinology *113:* 1173–1175 (1983).

4 Tannenbaum, G.S.; Ling, N.: The interrelationship of growth hormone (GH)-releasing factor and somatostatin in generation of the ultradian rhythm of GH secretion. Endocrinology *115:* 1952–1957 (1984).

5 Plotsky, P.M.; Vale, W.: Patterns of growth hormone-releasing factor and somatostatin secretion into the hypohysial portal circulation of the rat. Science *230:* 461–463 (1985).

6 Vance, M.L.; Kaiser, D.L.; Evans, W.S.; Furlanetto, R.; Vale, W.; Rivier, J.; Thorner, M.O.: Pulsatile growth hormone secretion in normal man during a continuous 24-hour infusion of human growth hormone releasing factor (1–40). J. clin. Invest. *75:* 1584–1590 (1985).

7 Tannenbaum, G.S.: Physiological role of somatostatin in regulation of pulsatile growth hormone secretion; in Patel, Tannenbaum, Somatostatin, pp. 229–259 (Plenum Press, New York, 1985).

8 Painson, J.-C.; Brazeau, P.; Lengyel, A.M.; Tannenbaum, G.S.: Interactions of somatostatin and growth hormone-releasing factor (GRF) in starvation. Program Int. Conf. Somatostatin, Washington 1986, p. 49.

9 Gurd, W.; Barrett, S.T.; Tannenbaum, G.S.: The interrelationship of somatostatin (SRIF) and growth hormone releasing factor (GRF) in mediation of growth hormone autofeedback. Program 67th Ann. Meet. Endocrine Society, 1985, A230.

10 Tannenbaum, G.S.; Guyda, H.J.; Posner, B.I.: Insulin-like growth factors: a role in growth hormone negative feedback and body weight regulation via brain. Science *220:* 77–79 (1983).

11 Berlowitz, M.; Szabo, M.; Frohman, L.A.; Firestone, S.; Chu, L.; Hintz, R.L.: Somatomedin-C mediates growth hormone negative feedback by effects on both the hypothalamus and the pituitary. Science *212:* 1279–1281 (1981).

12 Lumpkin, M.D.; Negro-Vilar, A.; McCann, S.M.: Paradoxical elevation of growth hormone by intraventricular somatostatin. Possible ultrashort-loop feedback. Science *211:* 1072–1074 (1981).

13 Peterfreund, R.A.; Vale, W.W.: Somatostatin analogs inhibit somatostatin secretion from cultured hypothalamus cells. Neuroendocrinology *39:* 397–402 (1984).

Dr. Gloria S. Tannenbaum
Neuropeptide Physiology Laboratory
Montreal Children's Hospital
2300 Tupper Street
Montreal, P.Q. H3H 1P3 (Canada)

Hormone Res. *29:* 75–78 (1988)

0301–0163/88/0293–0075$2.75/0

Physiological Significance of Gastrointestinal Somatostatin

V. Schusdziarra

Department of Internal Medicine II, Technical University of Munich, FRG

Key Words. Somatostatin · Stomach · Pancreas · Nutrient entry · Paracrine · Endocrine

Abstract. Somatostatin participates in the regulation of nutrient entry from the intestinal tract into the circulation. Thus, dietary fats and proteins may elicit significant increases of gastropancreatic somatostatin. Regulation of postprandial somatostatin secretion may occur via neural, hormonal and humoral factors. This peptide, in pharmacological doses, inhibits virtually all gastrointestinal exo- and endocrine functions as well as local motor activity. Neutralization of endogenous circulating somatostatin with specific antiserum is followed by increases in GH and enteroglucagon, augmenting also the postprandial rise of gastrin, insulin and pancreatic polypeptide. Somatostatin deficiency can be observed in obese subjects with hyperinsulinism. Concomitant elevation of insulin and gastrin levels can be antagonized by exogenous somatostatin. These findings confirm the importance of somatostatin as a peripheral regulator in experimental and human biology.

Introduction

Somatostatin immunoreactive material has been demonstrated to be present in D cells of the stomach, small intestine and pancreas. Additionally, it is present in vagal nerve fibres and in neurons of the submucosal and myenteric plexus of the gastrointestinal tract [1, 3]. This localization of somatostatin in organs which are responsible for the assimilation of ingested nutrients raises the possibility that somatostatin participates in the regulation of nutrient entry from the gastrointestinal tract into the circulation [4].

The following review will provide evidence for: (1) the release of somatostatin from D cells following the ingestion of a meal; (2) the regulation of postprandial somatostatin release by ingested and circulating nutrients, gut hormones, neuropeptides and local tissue factors; (3) the potential target organs for somatostatin as an endocrine or a paracrine factor, and (4) the potential pathogenetic role of somatostatin in obesity.

Release of Somatostatin into the Circulation

The ingestion of a mixed meal elicits a significant increase in peripheral vein plasma somatostatin levels in dogs and humans but not in rats [2, 4, 6–8]. The rise of peripheral somatostatin levels is the result of an increased somatostatin secretion from the pancreas and stomach while the contribution of the small intestine is uncertain. Major stimuli are fat and protein, both in dog and man, while carbohydrates elicit the smallest somatostatin response. The nutrient content is of major importance because simple volume distention by various water loads does not elicit any rise of somatostatin levels. Gastric acid is an important stimulus of somatostatin release in dogs whereas it may be of minor importance in humans. In rats acidification of the gastrointestinal tract has absolutely no stimulatory effect on gastric D cell function in vivo and in vitro [4, 5].

Regulation of Postprandial Somatostatin Secretion

Neural Mechanisms

Vagal stimulation elicits species-dependent stimulatory or inhibitory effects, respectively. In dogs electrical stimulation of the vagus augments somatostatin secretion, whereas in pigs, cats, and rats the same maneuver results in an inhibition [4, 5].

Cholinergic mechanisms participate in the stimulation of postprandial somatostatin release in dogs and man. Similar to vagal mechanisms, the effect of acetylcholine is species dependent. The infusion of acetylcholine stimulates gastric and pancreatic somatostatin release in dogs whereas in pigs and rats it is inhibited.

Adrenergic mechanisms stimulate postprandial somatostatin release in dogs, while in humans they are probably of minor importance. On the other hand, direct stimulation of the splanchnic nerves in dogs elicits an inhibitory effect on basal pancreatic somatostatin release.

Apart from the classical cholinergic and adrenergic neurotransmitter systems peptidergic neurotransmitters become increasingly important for regulatory phenomena in the gastrointestinal tract. Chemical and histological studies during the past 15 years have provided evidence for more than 30 peptide molecules that are present in the gastrointestinal tract. The vast majority of these peptides are located in neurons of the intrinsic nervous system which comprises the submucosal and the myenteric plexus. In spite of our increasing knowledge about the localisation of these peptides only little is known about their physiological role. This is mainly due to the fact that measurements of peptides which are secreted locally into the interstitial space are not measurable employing the available methods, and, secondly, they are in contrast to the classical neurotransmitters since virtually no specific receptor blockers are available that could antagonize the biological action of these peptides at the level of the target cell. One exception at the present moment is the existence of the specific opiate-receptor-blocking agent naloxone which antagonizes the effect of endogenous opioid active peptides such as enkephalins, β-endorphin and dynorphin.

In vitro naloxone-induced blockade of opiate receptors demonstrates that endogenous opioids participate in vagally-induced inhibition of somatostatin release from the isolated rat stomach. A similar effect as with naloxone is observed with acetylcholine. In vivo naloxone reduces the somatostatin response to protein, fat or carbohydrate test meals in dogs. During a combination of fat or protein meals with orally ingested or intravenously infused carbohydrates, respectively, naloxone stimulates postprandial somatostatin release in dogs and humans. This indicates that glucose elicits inhibitory mechanisms on D cell function via endogenous opioids. Similar effects have been shown previously for pancreatic polypeptide and insulin release in man. Other putative peptidergic neurotransmitters have been examined with regard to their effect on somatostatin release. Thus, bombesin, calcitonin-generated peptide (CGRP), vasoactive intestinal polypeptide (VIP), peptide histidine isoleucine (PHI), growth hormone-releasing factor (GRF) and substance P stimulate gastric somatostatin release. However, the effects observed with these exogenously infused peptides do not necessarily reflect the true biological action of the endogenously secreted material.

Intestinal Hormones

Gastric and pancreatic D cell function is stimulated by intestinal hormones such as gastric inhibitory polypeptide (GIP), motilin, CCK, and secretin. Interestingly, the effect of CCK and motilin is in part mediated by endogenous opioids.

Local Tissue Factors

Histamine activates D cell function via H_2-receptors. This might indicate a feedback system in which histamine stimulates acid secretion and simultaneously activates somatostatin, a major inhibitor of parietal cell function.

Furthermore, the additional acid-induced activation of gastric D cells is in part mediated by H_2-receptors. Prostaglandins contribute to postprandial somatostatin release in dogs while in rats they are mediators of the cholinergic inhibition of gastric D cell function.

Pancreatic Hormones and Circulating Nutrients

The islets of Langerhans contain four major hormones. Glucagon stimulates D cell function while the effect of pancreatic polypeptide is uncertain. Insulin is certainly the most important regulator of D cell function of pancreatic origin. It inhibits gastric as well as pancreatic D cell activity. The inhibitory effect of physiological elevations of plasma glucose on somatostatin levels is probably due to the inhibitory effect of simultaneously elevated insulin. On the other hand, amino acids stimulate pancreatic but not gastric somatostatin release, although it should be considered that physiological infusion rates of the various amino acids are largely unknown and therefore the physiological relevance of these findings has to await further evaluation [4, 5].

Effect of Somatostatin

Infusion Studies

Infusion of somatostatin at high pharmacological doses has been shown to have a potent inhibitory effect upon virtually all gastrointestinal and pancreatic exo- and endocrine functions as well as gastrointestinal motor activity [1, 4, 5]. While some target organs could be influenced by locally released somatostatin via paracrine mechanisms other functions would have to be regulated via circulating somatostatin (i.e. gallbladder contraction) due to the lack of somatostatin containing D cells in these organs. In addition, it is conceivable that paracrine and endocrine effects of somatostatin might act synergistically at the same target cell.

In vitro studies in the isolated dog pancreas have shown that low doses of somatostatin inhibit insulin and glucagon secretion. These data in the perfused pancreas indicate that A and B cells have a receptor population which is very sensitive towards low concentrations of somatostatin. Since receptor-binding studies have shown that down-regulation of somatostatin receptors occurs during exposure to high concentrations of somatostatin-14 and conversely depletion of endogenous somatostatin results in up-regulation of somatostatin-receptors, these sites cannot be exposed to the high concentrations of locally released somatostatin. It is very likely that tight junctions which have been demonstrated in the islets of Langerhans provide the basis for the separation of a somatostatin-rich compartment which comprises the locally or paracrine acting somatostatin from a somatostatin-poor compartment which permits biological effects of the much lower concentrations of circulating somatostatin. In analogy to these experiments studies in the isolated rat stomach have shown that low doses of somatostatin inhibit gastrin release. These in vitro studies strongly support the concept of an endocrine action of somatostatin in addition to a paracrine mode of action on the same target cells.

In vivo the infusion of synthetic somatostatin-14 at physiological rates, giving a rise of plasma somatostatin levels comparable to that observed after the ingestion of a meal, elicits inhibitory effects on several gastrointestinal functions such as gastric acid secretion, gastric emptying, pancreatic volume, bicarbonate and enzyme secretion, gallbladder emptying, glucose and triglyceride absorption and insulin glucagon, gastrin, GIP and pancreatic polypeptide secretion [4, 5]. These data support the concept of an endocrine action of postprandially released somatostatin. These infusion studies have been performed with somatostatin-14. Since in the postprandial state both molecular forms somatostatin-14 and somatostatin-28 are secreted into the circulation it will be necessary to examine additionally the biological effect of physiological doses of somatostatin-28.

Somatostatin Deficiency

In dogs the injection of an antisomatostatin serum acutely neutralizes the endogenous circulating somatostatin. Such an acute reduction of plasma SLI levels elicits an increase of basal growth hormone and enteroglucagon levels and augments the postprandial rise of plasma gastrin, insulin, pancreatic polypeptide and enteroglucagon while there is no effect on plasma GIP, glucagon and motilin levels. In addition, the postprandial rise of triglyceride levels is accelerated in this state of acute hyposomatostatinemia. These data strongly support the concept that circulating somatostatin attenuates the postprandial secretion of certain gastrointestinal hormones and retards the rate at which nutrients enter the circulation. Such an action of somatostatin as a 'shock absorber' would prevent an exaggerated and overshooting response of various secretory and/or motor functions in the gastrointestinal tract, thereby reducing perturbations of nutrient influx and facilitating the maintenance of nutrient homeostasis.

Somatostatin and Obesity

Somatostatin deficiency in humans can be observed in obese subjects with hyperinsulinism and normal glucose tolerance. Reduced basal and postprandial plasma somatostatin levels are associated with increased basal and postprandial plasma insulin and gastrin levels [6]. The infusion of somatostatin-14 restores in part circulating somatostatin in these obese subjects and decreases basal insulin and postprandial insulin and gastrin levels. Furthermore, the attenuated postprandial response of pancreatic polypeptide levels in the obese subjects is reduced even further during low dose somatostatin infusion [6]. These data demonstrate that deficiency of plasma somatostatin as observed in this group of obese subjects results in an increased sensitivity to infused somatostatin-14 indicating the possibility of an up-regulation of somatostatin receptors as already shown in different models. This is supportive evidence that in humans plasma somatostatin in the peripheral circulation is of biological importance.

In conclusion, several lines of evidence support the view that somatostatin is apart from any paracrine effect a true endocrine substance affecting its target cells via the circulation. The ingestion of a meal elicits an increase of peripheral circulating plasma somatostatin levels which can attenuate several gastrointestinal and pancreatic exo- and endocrine functions and which retards the rate of nutrient entry.

Thus, locally released somatostatin might affect one or the other individual function in the gastrointestinal tract via a paracrine mode of action while circulating somatostatin is an important factor of the regulation of nutrient influx and maintains together with insulin and glucagon secretion from the islets of Langerhans nutrient homeostasis.

References

1 McIntosh, C.; Arnold, R.: The radioimmunoassay and physiology of somatostatin in the pancreas and gastrointestinal tract. Z. Gastroenterol. *16:* 330 (1978).

2 Penman, E.; Wass, J.A.H.; Medbak, S.; Morgan, L.; Lewis, J.M.; Rees, L.H.; Besser, G.M.: Response of circulating immunoreactive somatostatin to nutritional stimuli in normal subjects. Gastroenterology *81:* 692 (1981).

3 Polak, J.M.; Grimelius, L.; Pearse, A.G.E.; Bloom, S.R.; Arimura, A.: Growth hormone release inhibiting hormone in gastrointestinal and pancreatic D-cells. Lancet *i:* 1220 (1975).

4 Schusdziarra, V.: Role of somatostatin in nutrient regulation; in Patel, Tannenbaum, Somatostatin, pp. 425–445 (Plenum Press, New York 1985).

5 Schusdziarra, V.; Schmid, R.: Physiological and pathophysiological aspects of somatostatin. Scand. J. Gastroent. *21:* suppl. 119, pp. 29–41 (1986).

6 Schusdziarra, V.; Lawecki, J.; Ditschuneit, H.H.; Lukas, B.; Maier, V.; Pfeiffer, E.F.: Effect of low-dose somatostatin infusion on pancreatic and gastric endocrine function in lean and obese nondiabetic human subjects, Diabetes *34:* 595–601 (1985).

7 Vinik, A.I.; Shapiro, B.; Glaser, B.; Wagner, L.: Circulating somatostatin in primates; in Bloom, Polak, Gut hormones, pp. 371–375 (Churchill Livingstone, Edinburgh 1981).

8 Wass, J.A.H.; Penman, E.; Dryburgh, J.R.: Tsiolakis, D.; Goldberg, P.L.; Dawson, A.M.; Besser, G.M.; Rees, L.H.: Circulating somatostatin after food and glucose in man. Clin. Endocr. *12:* 569 (1980).

Dr. V. Schusdziarra
Department of Internal Medicine II
Technical University of Munich
Ismaninger Strasse 22
D–8000 Munich 80 (FRG)

Hormone Res. *29:* 79–82 (1988)

0301–0163/88/0293–0079$2.75/0

Somatostatin Structure-Activity Studies in the Stomach

Barry H. Hirst[a], *Luis M. Botana*[b], *Eduardo Arilla*[c], *David H. Coy*[d]

[a] Department of Physiological Sciences, University of Newcastle upon Tyne, Medical School, Newcastle upon Tyne, UK;
[b] Departamento de Fisiologia Animal, Facultad de Veterinaria, Universidad de Santiago de Compostela, Spain;
[c] Departamento de Bioquimica, Facultad de Medicina, Universidad de Alcala de Henares, Spain;
[d] Peptide Research, Department of Medicine, Tulane University Medical Center, New Orleans, USA

Key Words. Gastric acid secretion · Pepsin secretion · Stomach · Somatostatin · Gastric inhibition

Abstract. Somatostatin may inhibit gastric exocrine functions independent of blockade of gastrin secretion. In order to further investigate this suppressive effect, somatostatin derivatives were injected to cats bearing a cannulated gastric fistula under pentagastrin stimulation. Results showed that somatostatin-14 was more potent than somatostatin-28 in this particular model. Analogues with substituted residues exhibited a variable spectrum of actions on hormone release and gastric function. A cyclic pentapeptide was deprived of gastric or GH inhibitory properties whereas the related peptide with a benzyl-protecting group on Thr was only devoid of gastric effect. The octapeptide SMS 201-995 was described as a potent inhibitor of gastric secretion in comparison with natural somatostatin in rats and also in humans, but was unable to induce maximal suppression of acid output in the cat model. Differences in gastric effect of different derivatives could be explained on the basis of binding to a selective subset of receptors, since at least two binding sites have been identified in the stomach mucosa. Serial studies with short cyclic somatostatin should help to establish a clear relationship between peptide structure and inhibition of gastric secretion.

Introduction

Somatostatin is a potent inhibitor of gastric endocrine and exocrine secretions in all species investigated. Early studies by Gomez-Pan et al. [1] from our laboratory demonstrated that the inhibition of gastric exocrine secretions, acid and pepsin, was a direct action independent of inhibition of gastrin release. The inhibition of food-stimulated acid secretion was also shown primarily to be by direct inhibition of acid secretion, in addition to the inhibition of gastrin release [2]. Somatostatin, however, shows some degree of selectivity in its ability to inhibit gastric acid secretion, being a potent inhibitor of secretion stimulated by pentagastrin, whilst only a poor inhibitor of secretion stimulated by histamine, both in vivo [3] and in vitro [4]. The inhibitory activity of somatostatin on the exocrine stomach is not mediated by prostaglandins, as somatostatin is still an effective inhibitor of gastric secretions after pretreatment with indomethacin [5]. Interest in the gastric potency of somatostatin analogues stems from the potential for suitable analogues as therapeutic agents in the management of upper gastrointestinal disease, including peptic ulceration and upper gastrointestinal haemorrhage.

Assay of Gastric Inhibitory Potency of Somatostatin and Analogues

The model we have used for investigating the gastric exocrine inhibitory potency of somatostatin and analogues is the conscious cat, previously prepared with cannulated gastric fistulae under full surgical anaesthesia. Gastric secretions are stimulated by a continuous infusion of a near-maximal gastric acid stimulatory dose of pentagastrin. Increasing doses of somatostatin or analogue are then added to the infusion, and the difference between secretory rates on control, without somatostatin, and test, with somatostatin, experiments the dose of somatostatin required for 50% inhibition (ID_{50}) can be determined. Over a number of years, we have found somatostatin to be a potent inhibitor of gastric acid secretion, as assayed by this method, with an ID_{50} of around 1.2–1.7 nmol/kg/h [6–8]. With pentagastrin as the stimulant of gastric secretions, somatostatin is approximately five times more potent an inhibitor of pepsin secretion compared with its effect on acid secretion [3, 5–8]. This apparent greater potency of somatostatin against pepsin secretion is due to the poor pepsin-stimulating activity of pentagastrin, rather than any specific effect of somatostatin; somatostatin is equipotent against acid and pepsin secretions stimulated by insulin, a much more potent stimulant of pepsin secretion [9].

Gastric Inhibitory Activities of Somatostatin-14 and Somatostatin-28

Somatostatin-14 is more potent than somatostatin-28 as an inhibitor of gastric exocrine secretions [8]. When expressed in terms of exogenous doses, somatostatin-14 is three to four times more potent than somatostatin-28. The difference is, however, enhanced to eight to nine times when expressed in terms of circulating concentrations of the two forms of somatostatin; e.g. ID_{50} for inhibition of acid secretion, SS-14, 232 p*M*; SS-28, 2,112 p*M*. The enhanced difference is due to the plasma immunoreactive half-life of SS-28 (6.1 min) being double that of SS-14 (2.4 min), probably due to the lower metabolic clearance rate of the latter. These data are consistent with a precursor role for somatostatin-28 in the stomach.

Somatostatin Analogues with Substituted Residues

We have investigated the gastric inhibitory potency of numerous somatostatin analogues over a number of years. In general, no selectivity between inhibition of gastric acid and pepsin secretions was evident; the analogues were always approximately five times more effective against pepsin secretion stimulated by pentagastrin. The results described below are summarized from several papers [6, 7, 10–12].

Trp^8 Substitutions

The importance of Trp^8 for somatostatin's activity in a number of systems has been highlighted. However, [*D*-Trp^8]somatostatin is only slightly more potent than the native peptide in the stomach, compared with the 6- to 8-fold increased endocrine inhibitory potency. Similarly, halogenated-Trp^8 analogues are up to 30 times more potent against growth hormone release in the rat (e.g. [*D*-5-Br-Trp^8]somatostatin), but are either equipotent, or show only slightly enhanced potency, against gastric secretions. Studies with position 8 modified analogues suggest that the electron density of the aromatic nucleus of Trp^8 may be relatively unimportant in determining gastric inhibitory activity, whilst the indole NH group plays a central role. Interestingly, whilst there are marked differences between the potency of position 8 substituted analogues for inhibition of endocrine, particularly growth hormone and insulin release, and gastric exocrine secretions, the gastric potencies are remarkably paralleled by their potency as inhibitors of electrically-induced contractions of the mouse vas deferens.

Lys^4 and Lys^9 Substitutions

Deletion of Lys^4, or substitution with an alcoholic (Thr) or acidic (Glu) residue yielded analogues with reduced (10% or less) potency compared with somatostatin. In comparison [Phe^4]somatostatin and modified Phe^4 analogues were approximately equipotent with somatostatin against gastric secretions. The high potency of Phe^4 analogues illustrates that the basic side-chain in position 4 is not essential for gastric activity. In contrast, substituting the lysine in position 9, including [p-NH_2-Phe^9]somatostatin, resulted in inactive analogues. Thus, the lysyl residue in position 9 is more critical than that in position 4 for somatostatin's gastric inhibitory activity.

Comparison of Gastric and Endocrine Potencies

With a variety of somatostatin analogues, the gastric inhibitory potencies can be separated from endocrine inhibitory potencies. An example with halogenated-Trp^8 analogues was described above. Other examples include [*D*-Cys^{14}]somatostatin (reduced insulin inhibitory activity), [Phe^4]somatostatin (reduced insulin and glucagon, and enhanced growth hormone inhibitory activities), [des-Asn^5, *D*-Trp^8, *D*-Ser^{13}]somatostatin (enhanced insulin, compared with reduced gastric, growth hormone and glucagon inhibitory activities), and [*D*-Ala^5, *D*-Trp^8]somatostatin (reduced gastric and glucagon, compared with enhanced growth hormone and insulin inhibitory activities). Comparisons such as those illustrated above raise the possibility that there is more than one class of somatostatin receptor, with differing pharmacological profiles. This might offer the opportunity of developing selective somatostatin analogues, useful therapeutically in the selective treatment of diseases as

Compound	Structure	Gastric inhibitory potency
Somatostatin	Ala¹ - Gly² - Cys³ - - - Phe⁶ - Phe⁷ - Trp⁸ / Cys¹⁴ - - - Phe¹¹ - Thr¹⁰ - Lys⁹	1.00
Salk octapeptide	Cys - Phe - Phe - Trp / Cys - Phe - Thr - Lys	<0.05
CGP 15425	Asn - Phe - Phe - Trp / GABA - Phe - Thr - Lys	0.06
CGP 16564 (MSD)	Phe - Phe - Trp / Phe - Thr - Lys	<0.01
CGP 24965 (MSD)	Pro - Phe - Trp / Phe - Thr - Lys	0.08
SMS 201-995	Phe - Cys - Phe - Trp / Thr - Cys - Thr - Lys	>1.00

1

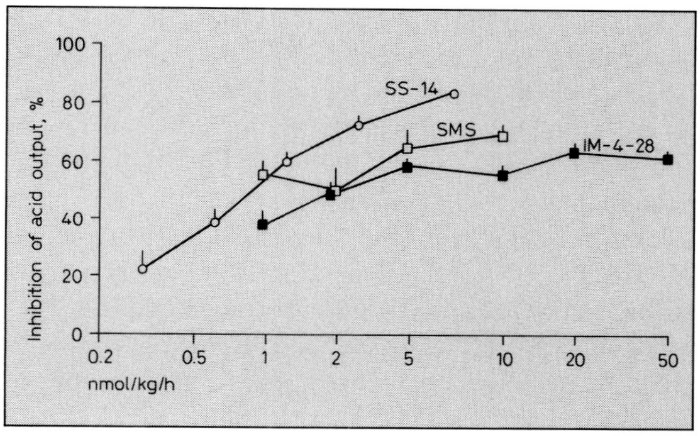

2

Fig. 1. Structure and gastric acid inhibitory potency of somatostatin analogues with reduced ring size. Gastric inhibitory potencies are compared with somatostatin. Amino acids in D configuration denoted by lower case. CGP denotes Ciba-Geigy Peptide supplied by Dr. R. H. Andreatta.

Fig. 2. Inhibition of gastric acid secretion by increasing doses of somatostatin-14 (SS-14), SMS 201-995 (SMS) and IM-4-28. See figure 1 and text for structures. Each point is mean with error bars of 1 SEM (n = 6). Methods as described in detail elsewhere [6–8].

diverse as acromegaly, diabetes and peptic ulceration. Whether the differential potency of somatostatin analogues truly reflects different classes of somatostatin receptors requires more detailed receptor studies in vitro. However, at least two classes of somatostatin-binding sites have been described by several laboratories, including data from our own in the rat [13], and human [14] brain, and rabbit stomach [15].

Somatostatin Analogues of Reduced Ring Size

A variety of short, cyclic analogues of somatostatin have been developed which retain marked inhibitory activity against growth hormone, insulin and glucagon secretion. The cyclic pentapeptide, cyclo(7-aminoheptanoyl-Phe-*D*-Trp-Lys-Thr), was without gastric or growth hormone inhibitory activity [16]. The related cyclic pentapeptide, with the benzyl protecting group on Thr retained, has been described by Coy et al. [17] as a somatostatin antagonist with respect to inhibition of growth hormone, insulin and glucagon release. However, this analogue shows neither antagonist nor agonist activity against gastric secretions [16]. Cyclic hexapeptides and octapeptides based on somatostatin can be synthesized, however, which do retain gastric inhibitory activity, if much reduced compared with the native tetradecapeptide (fig. 1).

Much recent effort has been directed into the study of the octapeptide analogue of somatostatin with a cyclic hexapeptide ring structure developed by Sandoz (SMS 201-995; fig. 1), as described in detail elsewhere in this volume. In the cat, SMS 201-995 is more potent than somatostatin as an inhibitor of gastric acid secretion, when compared at the 50% inhibition level. In the rat [18] and man [19], SMS 201-995 is also described as being more potent than somatostatin. However, SMS 201-995 is not able to produce maximal inhibition of gastric acid secretion in the cat. Doses of SMS 201-995 in the range 1–10 nmol/kg/h result in inhibition of acid secretion which is not dose-related, about 50–70% inhibition (fig. 2). We have observed similar non-maximal inhibition of acid secretion with CGP 24965 [16] and IM-4-28 (*D*-Phe-cyclo[Cys-Tyr-*D*-Trp-Lys-Val-Cys]-Thr (amide); fig. 2). In the rat cortex, SMS 201-995 has been described as interacting with only a subset of the high affinity somatostatin binding sites [18]. At least two binding sites have been identified in the gastric mucosa [15], but whether these are representative of somatostatin receptors involved in inhibition of gastric secretion, and whether SMS 201-995 can only bind to a sub-set, remain unanswered questions.

Several octapeptide analogues based on the structure of SMS 201-995 have been developed by Coy, and many of these show enhanced growth hormone inhibitory activity, in particular IM-4-28 [20]. However, in the cat in vivo, all demonstrate reduced gastric acid inhibitory potency compared with both somatostatin and SMS 201-995 [Botana and Hirst, unpubl. data]. Studies with these and other short cyclic analogues of somatostatin should help to define further structure-activity relationships for the inhibition of gastric secretion, as well as to categorize somatostatin receptors involved in differing systems.

References

1 Gomez-Pan, A.; Reed, J.D.; Albinus, M.; Shaw, B.; Hall, R.; Besser, G.M.; Coy, D.H.; Kastin, A.J.; Schally, A.V.: Direct inhibition of gastric acid and pepsin secretion by growth hormone-release inhibiting hormone in cats. Lancet *i:* 888–890 (1975).

2 Albinus, M.; Blair, E.L.; Grund, E.R.; Reed, J.D.; Sanders, D.J.; Gomez-Pan, A.; Schally, A.V.; Besser, G.M.: The mechanism whereby growth hormone-release inhibiting hormone (somatostatin) inhibits food stimulated gastric acid secretion in the cat. Agents and Actions *5:* 306–310 (1975).

3 Albinus, M.; Blair, E.L.; Hirst, B.H.; Reed, J.D.; Schally, A.V.; Shaw, B.: The effects of somatostatin and metiamide on tachyphylaxis of pentagastrin stimulated gastric acid and pepsin secretion in J. Physiol., Lond. *266:* 801–817 (1977).

4 Chew, C.S.: Inhibitory actions of somatostatin on isolated gastric glands and parietal cells. Am. J. Physiol. *G245:* G221–G229 (1983).

5 Albinus, M.; Gomez-Pan, A.; Hirst, B.H.; Shaw, B.: Evidence against prostaglandin-mediation of somatostatin-inhibition of gastric secretions. Regul. Pept. *10:* 259–266 (1985).

6 Brown, M.P.; Coy, D.H.; Gomez-Pan, A.; Hirst, B.H.; Hunter, M.; Meyers, C.; Reed, J.D.; Schally, A.V.; Shaw, B.: Structure-activity relationships of eighteen somatostatin analogues on gastric secretion. J. Physiol., Lond. *277:* 1–14 (1978).

7 Hirst, B.H.; Shaw, B.; Meyers, C.A.; Coy, D.H.: Structure-activity studies with somatostatin: the role of tryptophan in position 8. Regul. Pept. *1:* 97–113 (1980).

8 Hirst, B.H.; Conlon, J.M.; Coy, D.H.; Holland, J.; Shaw, B.: Comparison of the gastric exocrine inhibitory activities and plasma kinetics of somatostatin-28 and somatostatin-14 in cats. Regul. Pept. *4:* 227–237 (1982).

9 Hirst, B.H.; Reed, J.D.; Shaw, B.; Coy, D.H.; Schally, A.V.: Quantitation of somatostatin inhibition of insulin-stimulated gastric acid and pepsin secretion in the cat. Acta hepato-gastroent. *25:* 208–212 (1978).

10 Reed, J.D.; Hirst, B.H.; Gomez-Pan, A.; Coy, D.H.; Schally, A.V.: Meyers, C.: Inhibition of gastric acid secretion by stereoisomers of somatostatin. Metabolism *27:* 1411–1413 (1978).

11 Hirst, B.H.; Reed, J.D.; Shaw, B.; Hayward, C.F.; Morley, J.S.: Non-reducible cyclic, and azaphenylalanyl^6 analogues of somatostatin. Eur. J. Pharmacol. *65:* 151–156 (1980).

12 Hirst, B.H.; Coy, D.H.: Structure-activity studies with somatostatin: role of lysine in positions 4 and 9 for gastric activity. Regul. Pept. *8:* 267–271 (1984).

13 Weightman, D.R.; Whitford, C.A.; Snell, C.R.; Hirst, B.H.; Brundish, D.E.; Kendall-Taylor, P.A.: Rat brain membranes possess two high affinity binding sites for [^{3}H]somatostatin. Neurosci. Lett. *55:* 161–166 (1985).

14 Whitford, C.A.; Bloxham, S.A.; Snell, C.R.; Candy, J.M.; Hirst, B.H.: Regional distribution of high-affinity [^{3}H]somatostatin binding sites in the human brain. Brain Res. *398:* 141–147 (1986).

15 Guijarro, L.G.; Arilla, E.; Lopez-Ruiz, M.P.; Prieto, J.C.; Whitford, C.; Hirst, B.H.: Somatostatin binding sites in cytosolic fraction isolated from rabbit antral and fundic gastric mucosa. Regul. Pept. *10:* 207–215 (1985).

16 Hirst, B.H.; Arilla, E.; Coy, D.H.; Shaw, B.: Cyclic hexa- and pentapeptide somatostatin analogues with reduced gastric inhibitory activity. Peptides *5:* 857–860 (1984).

17 Coy, D.H.; Murphy, W.A.; Lance, V.A.; Hocart, S.J.; Sueiras-Diaz, J.; Mezo, I.: Somatostatin agonists and antagonists – peptide control of growth hormone secretion; in Patel, Tannenbaum, Somatostatin, pp. 325–337 (Plenum Press, New York 1985).

18 Pless, J.; Bauer, W.; Briner, U.; Doepfner, W.; Marbach, P.; Maurer, R.; Petcher, T.J.; Reubi, J.-C.; Vonderscher, J.: Chemistry and pharmacology of SMS 201–995, a long-acting octapeptide analogue of somatostatin. Scand. J. Gastroent. *21:* suppl. 119, pp. 54–64 (1986).

19 Gyr, K.E.; Whitehouse, I.; Beglinger, C.; Kohler, E.; Dettwiler, S.; Fried, M.: Human pharmacological effects of SMS 201–995 on gastric secretion. Scand. J. Gastroent. *21:* suppl. 119, pp. 96–102 (1986).

20 Murphy, W.A.; Heiman, M.L.; Lance, V.A.; Mezo, I.; Coy, D.H.: Octapeptide analogs of somatostatin exhibiting greatly enhanced in vivo and in vitro inhibition of growth hormone secretion in Biochem. biophys. Res. Commun. *132:* 922–928 (1985).

Dr. Barry H. Hirst
Department of Physiological Sciences
University of Newcastle upon Tyne
Newcastle upon Tyne NE2 4HH (UK)

Hormone Res. *29:* 83–85 (1988)

0301-0163/88/0293-0083$2.75/0

Hormonal and Nonhormonal Cytoprotective Effect by Somatostatins

K.H. Usadel

II. Medizinische Klinik, Klinikum Mannheim, University of Heidelberg, FRG

Key Words. Somatostatin · Cytoprotection · Tissue damage · Cell membrane

Abstract. Beside its known hormonal activity, somatostatin exerts cytoprotective action. Thus, its favorable effect on the course of experimental pancreatitis, liver and lung lesions, and gastric ulcerations cannot be explained solely on the basis of hormone-mediated mechanisms. Cytoprotection is only observed when somatostatin is administered prior to toxine exposure or tissue damage, and the structure/activity of the substance is important in determining this effect. Thus, the non-hormonal biological effects of somatostatin can be summarized as follows: (a) Natural somatostatin-14 has been shown, in addition to its full endocrine effect, to block the uptake of toxic substances into liver cells. (b) Analogues with superactive cytoprotection may be devoid of endocrine activity. In turn, this effect is commonly found in the low-molecular derivatives. (c) Although the mechanism leading to tissue protection has not been clarified, stabilisation of cell membranes may play a role as well as changes in the aminoacid sequence.

Ethanol, acids, bases, histamine and other compounds of completely different structure can injure gastric mucosa after oral administration in experimental animals and humans [1]. Changes include hemorrhagic lesions and necrosis of the epithelium. Prostaglandins, H_2-receptor blockers, sulfhydryls, somatostatin and some analogues of somatostatin will protect gastric and duodenal mucosa in such experimental ulcer models [1–8]. This tissue protection is independent of acid secretion. It was called 'cytoprotection' and recently redefined by experts [9] as: 'Organ specific reduction or prevention of vulnerability of cells and tissues against injury for cell preservation in vitro and in vivo.'

Several findings suggest that beside hormonal efficacy somatostatin exerts cytoprotective action. Several clinical indications for treatment with somatostatin are based on its abilities to inhibit specific secretions in the GI tract. Thus, somatostatin has a favorable effect on the course of experimental acute pancreatitis, gastric ulcers, erosions as well as on duodenal ulcers in animals and humans [6]. Mortality rates are also reduced by somatostatin in experimental models, but suppression of GI secretion may not be the only mechanism by which somatostatin protects tissues from damage. Beneficial effects were seen in lung lesions after cysteamine, alpha-amanitine and diphtheria toxin, in adrenal necrosis after diphtheria toxin and cysteamine, in liver necrosis after phalloidin and galactosamine, and in other experimental shock models, e.g. *Escherichia coli* endotoxin, and antitumor drug intoxications [7]. All these experimentally induced injuries were ameliorated by somatostatin pretreatment, and it has therefore been suggested by us that somatostatin has a local cytoprotective effect. This effect may be exerted only if administered in advance of toxin exposure. This is supported by the fact that treatment of patients with acute pancreatitis in a multicenter double-blind trial has not shown a significant difference between somatostatin versus placebo [10]. Pancreatitis was already present when the patients were admitted to the hospitals, and possibly cytoprotection could not be achieved. On the other hand, somatostatin is thought to be an efficient therapeutic tool for preventing acute pancreatitis after cholangiopancreatography [11].

Several double-blind trials have proven the efficacy of somatostatin in upper GI bleeding [12, 13], but the mechanism of its action is not fully understood. It has been postulated that somatostatin protects nondamaged mucosal cells, and promotes regeneration of the mucosa.

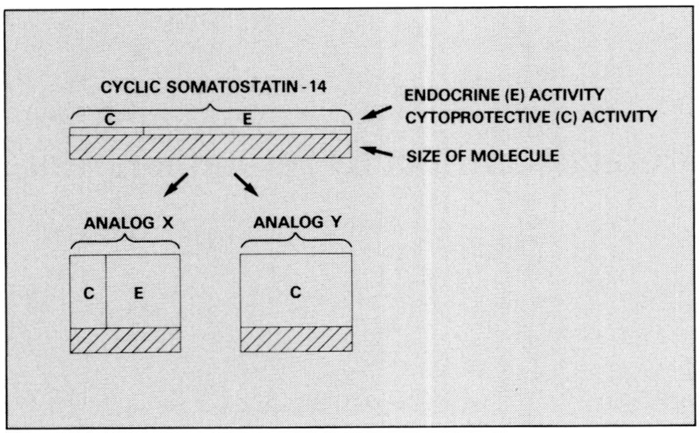

Fig. 1. Scheme of molecular size and biological activities of somatostatins. In analogue X decreased size of the molecule is accompanied by increase of endocrine and cytoprotective properties. Analogue Y represents supercytoprotective action with loss of endocrine activity.

Furthermore, several additional mechanisms may be involved such as inhibition of acid secretion and reduction of splanchnic blood flow. Our own experience using various experimental models which lead to parenchymal lesions [7] has additionally shown that only pretreatment or very early treatment with somatostatin exerts cytoprotection. This is especially true for gastric and hepatic lesions [8].

Of importance in determining the mechanisms of somatostatin effect is the structure/activity of the compound. Analogues of somatostatin with increased potency for the inhibition of hormone secretion have been synthesized. Effectiveness in the management of acromegaly and other conditions will be discussed elsewhere in this symposium.

Since somatostatin-14 exerts at least two principally different modes of action namely inhibition of hormonal secretion and cytoprotection, we have raised the question whether these actions of somatostatin analogues can be dissociated.

An important effect of somatostatin and some analogues was described by Ziegler et al. [14]. Synthesis and conformation studies of analogues used were described by Kessler et al. [15]. It could be demonstrated that cyclic somatostatin-14 inhibits the uptake of phallotoxins and of cholic acids in isolated liver cells in a concentration-dependent manner. Some cyclic hexapeptide analogues inhibited very strongly both kinds of transport. The inhibition of cholate uptake was thought to be unlikely a hormonal effect of somatostatin, because concentrations needed were about 1,000-fold higher than circulating levels. This suggests the existence of non endocrine receptor-mediated but cell membrane located effects which might be responsible for cytoprotection. Rao et al. [16] demonstrated that bleb formation of rat hepatocytes in vitro occurs after addition of various toxins especially phalloidin. Dose-dependent cytoprotection could be achieved either by somatostatin-14 or by various analogues. Investigations by Ziegler et al. [14] are in agreement with these results. It could be shown that an increase of activity of the analogues occurred in both experimental models.

It has been reported earlier that the amino acid sequence -Phe-*D*-Trp-Lys-Thr- is responsible for the endocrine activity of somatostatins [17]. This sequence is also present in the analogues of somatostatin which are endocrinologically more active, but there are analogues of somatostatin with drastic increase of cytoprotection but loss of endocrine activity. This increase of cytoprotective properties could be achieved only by retroinverse sequence of amino acids [18] of several hexapeptide analogues. Superactive analogues on cytoprotection do not need the above mentioned sequence of 4 amino acids which is responsible for endocrine activity.

From these data we draw the following conclusions: (a) somatostatins are biologically active in a cyclic conformation, and (b) for the endocrine effect the amino acid sequence -Phe-*D*-Trp-Lys-Thr- of the molecule is essential. Conformation is also essential for cytoprotection. The molecule may contain the total amino acid sequence of B, but this is *not* required for cytoprotection.

Our preliminary findings indicate that analogues of somatostatin reveal cytoprotective properties also under experimental in vivo conditions such as cerulein- or tauro-cholate-induced experimental pancreatitis, ethanol-induced gastric hemorrhagic erosions, and cysteamine-induced duodenal ulceration in rats [19]. These beneficial effects were seen by the use of low doses of the analogues.

Concerning the molecular size and biological activities of somatostatins the following hypothesis can be postulated (fig. 1). In the development of somatostatin analogues an increase of biological activity could be achieved in two ways: (1) if endocrine activity is potentiated the cytoprotective activity is potentiated as well, and (2) in analogues with superactive cytoprotection the endocrine activity is lost. In both, molecular size is smaller (hexa-, octapeptides) in comparison to regular somatostatin which contains 14 amino acids. Whether the stimulation of phagocytosis in reticular endothelial cells as reported by Szabo [20] is also due to the cytoprotective action of some somatostatin derivatives is still unclear but 'stabilisation' of cell membranes (cytosceleton) as a result of cytoprotection might also be responsible for this effect. More investigations are needed to clarify the question whether cytoprotection of somatostatins is important for clinical use.

References

1 Robert, A.; Nezamis, J.E.; Lancaster, C.; Hanchar, A.J.: Cytoprotection by prostaglandins in rats. Prevention of gastric necrosis produced by alcohol, HCl, NaOH, hypertonic NaCl and thermal injury. Gastroenterology *77:* 433–443 (1979).

2 Miller, T.A.: Protective effects of prostaglandins against gastric mucosal damage. Current knowledge and proposed mechanism. Am. J. Physiol. G *245:* G601–623 (1983).

3 Robert, A.: Cytoprotection by prostaglandins. Gastroenterology *77:* 761–767 (1979).

4 Lacy, E.R.; Ito, S.: Microscopic analysis of ethanol damage to rat gastric mucosa after treatment with a prostaglandin. Gastroenterology *83:* 619–625 (1982).

5 Szabo, S.; Trier, J.S.; Frankel, P.W.: Sulfhydryl compounds may mediate gastric cytoprotection. Science *214:* 200–202 (1981).

6 Schwedes, U.; Usadel, K.H.; Szabo, S.: Cysteamine-induced duodenal ulcer: prevention by somatostatin (SRIF). Eur. J. Pharmacol. *44:* 195–196 (1977).

7 Usadel, K.H.; Schwedes, U.; Wdowinski, J.M.: Pharmacological effects of somatostatin in acute organ lesions. Inn. Med. *9:* 204–208 (1982).

8 Szabo, S.; Usadel, K.H.: Cytoprotection – organoprotection by somatostatin: gastric and hepatic lesions. Experientia *38:* 254–256 (1982).

9 Usadel, K.H.: Conclusions of international symposium on mechanism of cell injury, cytoprotection – organoprotection. Klin. Wschr. *64:* suppl. 7, p. 155 (1985).

10 Usadel, K.H.; Ueberla, K.K.; Leuschner U.: Treatment of acute pancreatitis with somatostatin. Results of the multicenter double-blind trial (APTS-Study). Dig. Dis. Sci. *30:* 992 (1985).

11 Cicero, G.F. Laugier, R.; Sahel, J.; Manganaro, M.; Sarles H.: Effects of somatostatin on clinical, biochemical and morphological changes following ERCP. Ital. J. Gastroent. *17:* 265–270 (1985).

12 Magnusson, I.; Ihre, T.; Johansson, C.; Seligson, U.; Torngren, S.; Uvnas-Moberg, K.: Randomised double blind trial of somatostatin in the treatment of massive upper gastrointestinal haemorrhage. Gut *26:* 221–226 (1985).

13 Antonioli, A.; Gandolfo, M.; Rigo, G.P.; Bianchi Porro, G.; Cheli, R.; Brancato, F.; Lazzaroni, M.; Parodi, M.C.; Maringhini, A.; Raimondo, S.; Manenti, F.: Somatostatin and cimetidine in the control of acute upper gastrointestinal bleeding. A controlled multicenter study. Hepato-gastroenterology, *33:* 71–74 (1986).

14 Ziegler, K.; Frimmer, M.; Kessler, H.; Damm, J.; Eiermann, V.; Koll, S.; Zarbock, J.: Modified somatostatin as inhibitors of a multispecific transport system for bile acids and phallotoxins in isolated hepatocytes. Biochim. biophys. Acta *845:* 86–93 (1985).

15 Kessler, H.; Bernd, M.; Damm, I.: Peptide confirmations, NMR investigations of cyclic hexapeptides containing the active sequence of somatostatin. Tetrahedron Lett. *23:* 4685–4688 (1982).

16 Rao, G.S.; Lemnoch H.; Kessler, H.; Damm, I.; Knoll, S.; Usadel, K.H.: Cytoprotection by novel synthetic analogues of somatostatin. Acta endocr., Copenh. *105:* suppl. 264, p. 96 (1984).

17 Vale, W.; Rivier, J.; Ling, N.; Brown, M.: Biologic and immunologic activities and applications of somatostatin analogs. Metabolism *27:* suppl. 1, pp. 1391–1401 (1978).

18 Kessler, H.; Gehrke, M.; Haupt, A.; Klein, M.; Müller, A.; Wagner, K.: Common structural features for cytoprotection activities of somatostatin antamanide and related peptides. Klin. Wschr. *64:* suppl. 7, pp. 74–78 (1986).

19 Usadel, K.H.; Kessler, H.; Rohr, G.; Kusterer, K.; Palitzsch, K.D.; Schwedes, U.: Cytoprotective properties of somatostatins. Klin. Wschr. *64:* suppl. 7, pp. 59–63 (1986).

20 Szabo, S.: Somatostatin stimulates clearance and hepatic uptake of colloidal carbon in the rat. Life Sci. *33:* 1975–1980 (1983).

Dr. K.H. Usadel
II. Medizinische Klinik
Klinikum Mannheim der Universität Heidelberg
Theodor-Kutzer-Ufer
D-8600 Mannheim 1 (FRG)

Hormone Res. 29: 86–88 (1988)

0301–0163/88/0293–0086$2.75/0

Measurement of Somatostatin

J.A.H. Wass

Department of Endocrinology, St. Bartholomew's Hospital, London, UK

Key Words. Somatostatin · Biological activity · Tissue contents · Radioimmunoassay

Abstract. Biological activity of somatostatin can be altered by modifications in the amino acid sequence. Thus, a number of bioassays have been developed in order to measure the potency and specificity of analogues and heterogenous molecular forms of somatostatin. These procedures may assist in the estimation of somatostatin contents of tissue extracts but measurements in blood are limited by the presence of other substances masking the biological response to somatostatin. Recently, radioimmunoassay procedures have been developed and their usefulness in experimental and clinical medicine is reviewed.

Introduction

The identification of somatostatin has been characterized by marked structural heterogeneity. Thus, Schally et al. [1] found 3 different molecular weight forms of somatostatin which were all biologically active. Arimura et al. [2] chromatographed extracts of rat stomach and pancreas and again found both tissues to contain high molecular weight forms of somatostatin as well as the tetradecapeptide form. In the hypothalamus all groups have reported a 1.6-kilodalton form together with 3 kilodaltons and higher molecular weight forms. Both the intermediate and high molecular weight forms do not break down during treatment with dithiothreitol, an agent which reduces disulphide bonds, indicating that they do not represent aggregates of the tetradecapeptide. Somatostatin-28 was described by Pradayrol et al. [3]. This has a molecular weight of 3,145 daltons and contains the amino acid sequence of tetradecapeptide somatostatin extended by 14 residues at the N-terminus. The two consecutive basic residues located just before the cleavage site that produce tetradecapeptide suggested that this may be a precursor to somatostatin-14. However, different quantities of somatostatin-28 and varying ratios of somatostatin-28 and somatostatin-14 in different tissues together with other evidence suggests that while it may be a precursor, it also acts as a hormone in its own right with its own somewhat different spectrum of activity in different tissues.

In the following the biological activity and the measurement of circulating somatostatin will be discussed.

Structural Requirements for Somatostatin Bioactivity

Both linear and cyclic somatostatin have bioactivity in vitro [4]. The amino-terminus is not required for activity. Analogues which cannot form a covalent cyclic structure because the cysteine residues are either substituted by alanine or in cases where the sulphydril groups have been alkylated, exhibit greatly reduced but still significant bioactivity. This suggests that the disulphide bond is probably necessary for interaction with the receptor. Although the disulphide bond is important, the size of the ring is not critical. The amino acid residues seen in positions 7–10 appear to be essential and in general the length of action can be increased by substituting tryptophan in position 8. Thus, analogues of somatostatin have been synthesized that are more potent, longer acting and more specific than the native peptide. Some inhibit insulin more effectively than glucagon and vice versa and it has been found that increased growth hormone suppression can be obtained. Inhibition of gastrin secretion appears to involve unique structural requirements. Because of these variations it seems possible that there are differences in the structure requirements of somatostatin receptors on the alpha- and beta-cells of the gastrointestinal tract and pituitary cells.

Bioassay

Because of its broad spectrum of biological action, a number of bioassays for the peptide have been developed which depend on suppression of growth hormone, insulin, or glucagon secretion [5–7]. They are useful for measuring the biological potency of synthetic somatostatin preparations, analogues and the heterogenous molecular forms of somatostatin. They are used for measuring somatostatin content of tissue extracts but measurement in blood is limited by the presence of other hormones and biologically active peptides which interfere with these biological responses.

Radioimmunoassay

The first radioimmunoassay of somatostatin was reported by Arimura et al. [8]. For measurement of somatostatin in tissues most laboratories use a non-extracted radioimmunoassay. There are large discrepancies between the estimates of somatostatin tissue content by different laboratories even when tissues from the same species are compared (table I). The differences may be due to a number of factors, including the use of several antibodies differently affected by the presence of somatostatin-binding protein in tissues, different methods of storage and extraction of tissues, and different purity of synthetic somatostatin preparations used as standards for the assays [9].

The radioimmunoassay of somatostatin in blood presents several problems. Endogenous somatostatin is rapidly degraded in the presence of plasma and this is also true for the iodinated somatostatin tracer. Because of this and the fact that somatostatin binds to a high molecular weight protein which is present in the circulation, it is now generally agreed that in order to be measured accurately somatostatin must first be extracted from plasma, and there are a variety of methods [9]. Using extraction basal circulating somatostatin levels are usually below 100 pg/ml. Values recorded in normal subjects and in patients with different conditions are recorded in table II. Levels when measured in patients with tumours secreting somatostatin are much higher,

Table I. Somatostatin levels in different locations in rat and man

Location	Species	Level ng/mg net weight of tissue	Reference
Hypo-thalamus	rat	2.12	Brownstein et al. [11], 1975
	rat	1.11	Kronheim et al. [12], 1976
	rat	2.3	Patel and Reichlin [13], 1978
Pancreas	rat	0.14	Arimura et al. [2], 1975
	rat	0.34	Vale et al. [14], 1976
	rat	0.033	McIntosh et al. [15], 1978
	man	0.25	McIntosh et al. [15], 1978
Stomach (fundus)	rat	0.46	Arimura et al. [2], 1975
	rat	0.046	McIntosh et al. [15], 1978
	man	0.60	Chayvialle et al. [16], 1978
	man	0.29	McIntosh et al. [15], 1978
Stomach (antrum)	rat	0.43	Arimura et al. [2], 1975
	rat	0.050	McIntosh et al. [15], 1978
	man	1.68	Chayvialle et al. [16], 1978
	man	0.46	McIntosh et al. [15], 1978
Duodenum	rat	0.025	Arimura et al. [2], 1975
	rat	0.15	Patel and Reichlin [13], 1978
	man	1.35	Chayvialle et al. [16], 1978

Table II. Published normal ranges for peripheral plasma somatostatin levels in different species

Species	Somatostatin range, pg/ml	Reference
Man	174±9 (92%)	Kronheim et al. [17], 1978
	1,000±41 (8%)	
	88±8	Krejs et al. [10], 1979
	80±25*	Lundqvist et al. [18], 1979
	675±95**	Pipeleers et al. [19], 1979
	11.9±1.6	Saito et al. [20], 1980
Rat	10.5±2.6	Arimura et al. [21], 1978
Pig	138±20	Gustavsson and Lundqvist [22], 1978
Dog	119.7±7.6	Schusdziarra et al. [23], 1977
	10	Arimura et al. [24], 1978
	28.5±8.4	Chayvialle et al. [25], 1978

Values quoted are the mean of the normal range ± 1 SEM except for * where values are quoted as the mean ± 1 SD and ** for which limits of range are not given.

ranging up to 25,000 ng/ml. These assays have established that some non-pancreatic tumours secrete the peptide and abnormal secretion has been demonstrated in lung and thyroid tumours [10]. Determination procedures, however, are still laborious and do not allow its use on a routine basis.

References

1 Schally, A.V.; Dupont, A.; Arimura, A.; Redding, T.W.; Lithincum, G.L.: Isolation of porcine GH release inhibiting hormone (GH-RIH): the existence of 3 forms of GH-RIH. Fed. Proc. *34:* 584 (1975).

2 Arimura, A.; Sato, H.; Dupont, A.; Nishi, N.; Schally, A.V.: Somatostatin: Abundance of immunoreactive hormone in rat stomach and pancreas. Science *189:* 1007–1009 (1975).

3 Pradayrol, L.; Jörnvall, H.; Mutt, V.; Ribet, A.: N-terminally extended somatostatin: The primary structure of somatostatin-28. FEBS Lett. *109:* 55–58 (1980).

4 Brazeau, P.; Vale, W.; Burgus, R.; Ling, N.; Butcher, R.; Rivier, J.; Guillemin, R.: Hypothalamic polypeptide that inhibits the secretion of immunoreactive pituitary growth hormone. Science *178:* 77–79 (1973).

5 Vale, W.; Brazeau, P.; Rivier, C.; Brown, M.; Boss, B.; Rivier, J.; Burgus, R.; Ling, N.; Guillemin, R.: Somatostatin. Recent Prog. Horm. Res. *31:* 365–397 (1975).

6 Bhathena, S.J.; Perrino, P.V.; Voyles, N.R.; Smith, S.S.; Wilkins, S.D.; Coy, D.H.; Schally, A.V.; Recant, L.: Reversal of somatostatin inhibition of insulin and glucagon secretion. Diabetes *25:* 1031–1040 (1976).

7 Rivier, J.; Brazeau, P.; Vale, W.; Guillemin, R.: Somatostatin analogs. Relative importance of the disulphide bridge and of the Ala-Gly side chain for biological activity. J. med. Chem. *18:* 123–126 (1975).

8 Arimura, A.; Sato, H.; Coy, D.H.; Schally, A.V.: Radioimmunoassay for GH-release inhibiting hormone. Proc. Soc. exp. Biol. Med. *148:* 784–789 (1975).

9 Penman, E.; Wass, J.A.H.; Lund, A.; Lowry, P.J.; Stewart, J.K.; Dawson, A.M.; Besser, G.M.; Rees, L.H.: Development and validation of the specific radioimmunoassay for somatostatin in human plasma. Ann. clin. Biochem. *16:* 15–25 (1979).

10 Krejs, G.J.; Orci, L.; Conlon, J.M.; Ravazzola, M.; Davis, G.R.; Raskin, P.; Collins, S.M.; McCarthy, D.M.; Baetens, D.; Rubenstein, A.; Aldor, T.A.M.; Unger, R.H.: Somatostatinoma syndrome: Biochemical, morphologic and clinical features. New Engl. J. Med. *301:* 285–292 (1979).

11 Brownstein, M.; Arimura, A.; Sato, H.; Schally, A.V.; Kizer, J.S.: The regional distribution of somatostatin in the rat brain. Endocrinology *96:* 1456–1461 (1975).

12 Kronheim, S.; Berelowitz, M.; Pimstone, B.L.: A radioimmunoassay for growth hormone release-inhibiting hormone: Method and quantitative tissue distribution. Clin. Endocrinol. *5:* 619–630 (1976).

13 Patel, Y.C.; Reichlin, S.: Somatostatin in hypothalamus, extra hypothalamic brain and peripheral tissues of the rat. Endocrinology *102:* 523–530 (1978).

14 Vale, W.; Ling, N.; Rivier, J.; Villarreal, J.; Rivier, C.; Douglas, C.; Brown, M.: Anatomic and philogenetic distribution of somatostatin. Metabolism *25:* suppl. 1, pp. 1491–1494 (1976).

15 McIntosh, C.; Arnold, R.; Bothe, E.; Becker, H.; Köbberling, J.; Creutzfeldt, W.: Gastrointestinal somatostatin: Extraction and radioimmunoassay in different species. Gut *19:* 655–663 (1978).

16 Chayvialle, J.A.P.; Descos, F.; Bernard, C.; Martin, A.; Barb, E.C.; Portensky, C.: Somatostatin in mucosa of stomach and duodenum in gastroduodenal disease. Gastroenterology *75:* 13–19 (1978).

17 Kronheim, S.; Berelowitz, M.; Pimstone, B.L.: The characterisation of somatostatin-like immuno-reactivity in human serum. Diabetes *27:* 523–529 (1978).

18 Lundqvist, G.; Gustavsson, S.; Hällgren, R.: Plasma levels of somatostatin-like immunoreactivity independence of kidney function. Clin. Endocrinol. *10:* 489–492 (1979).

19 Pipeleers, D.; Somers, G.; Gepts, W.; Nutt, N. de; De Vroede, M.: Plasma pancreatic hormone levels in a case of somatostatinoma: diagnostic and therapeutic implications. J. clin. Endocr. Metab. *49:* 572–579 (1979).

20 Saito, H.; Ogawa, T.; Ishmaru, K.; Oshima, I.; Saito, S.: Plasma somatostatin in normal and diseased states. Program VIth Int. Congr. Endocrinol., Melbourne 1980, abst. 75.

21 Arimura, A.; Lundqvist, G.; Rothman, J.; Chang, R.; Fernandez-Durango, R.; Elde, R.; Coy, D.H.; Meyers, C.; Schally, A.V.: Radioimmunoassay of somatostatin. Metabolism *27:* suppl. 1, pp. 1139–1144 (1978).

22 Gustavsson, S.; Lundqvist, G.: Participation of antral somatostatin in the local regulation of gastrin release. Acta endocr., Copenh. *88:* 329–346 (1987).

23 Schusdziarra, V.; Dobbs, R.E.; Harris, V.; Unger, R.H.: Immunoreactive somatostatin levels in plasma of normal and alloxan diabetic dogs. FEBS Lett *81:* 69–72 (1977).

24 Arimura, A.; Itoh, Z.; Aizawa, I.; Rothman, J.: Radioimmunoassay for plasma somatostatin and its application in studying somatostatin release from dog stomach. Prog. 60th Meet. Endocrine Soc., Miami 1978, abstr. 155.

25 Chayvialle, J.A.; Miyata, M.; Rayford, P.L.; Thompson, J.C.: Effect of food ingestion on vasoactive intestinal peptide and somatostatin plasma levels in control and antrectomised dogs. Scand. J. Gastroent. *13:* suppl. 49, p. 37 (1978).

Dr. J.A.H. Wass
Department of Endocrinology
St. Bartholomew's Hospital
London EC1A 7BE (UK)

Hormone Res. *29:* 89–91 (1988)

0301–0163/88/0293–0089$2.75/0

Clinical Applications of Somatostatin

Emilio del Pozo

Experimental Therapeutics Department, Clinical Research, Sandoz AG, Basle, Switzerland

Key Words. Somatostatin · Central nervous system · Pituitary hormones · Peripheral effect · Miscellaneous indications

Abstract. Because of its wide distribution in the organism, natural somatostatin (SRIF) demonstrates an ample spectrum of actions, involving mainly the central neuroendocrine system and the enteropancreatic area. In the former, this peptide may find its field of application in conditions characterized by excessive GH, TSH or ACTH secretion, depending on the central or peripheral cause of the inappropriate hormone control. The inhibitory effect of SRIF on gastrointestinal and pancreatic hormones may be useful in the management of tumors originating in this system and also in the treatment of inflammatory processes such as pancreatitis, in malignant diarrhea, and in gastrointestinal bleeding. A complex action of SRIF and its derivative on insulin release and glucose homeostasis may offer some advantages in the control of unstable diabetes. Dampening of organic functions in the upper digestive tract may also render SRIF and its analogues useful in the exploration of the gallbladder, gastric and pancreatic functions. The effect of such peptides on tissue growth and on the regulation of blood pressure are the subject of present investigations. Cytoprotection, an interesting aspect of SRIF application, is discussed elsewhere in this compendium. Finally, some comments on the possible use of SRIF as an additive to the conventional treatment of burns and sepsis close this review.

Since its characterization from hypothalamic extracts in the early seventies, the endocrine profile of natural somatostatin (SRIF) has been thoroughly investigated. Because of its wide distribution, SRIF demonstrates an ample spectrum of actions, which mainly involve the central neuroendocrine system and the gastroenteropancreatic area. In addition, binding sites for this peptide have been detected in a number of structures and systems suggesting a role in the control of autonomous nervous functions and in the production of hormones among others. However, it is not clear whether such effects represent physiological actions or are merely pharmacological in nature.

Recently, Bauer et al. [1] have synthetized SMS 201-995 (Sandostatin), a cyclic octapeptide, which is highly resistant to degradation and exhibits an action profile similar to the natural peptide. Experiments conducted in animals and in man have shown this substance to be about 70 and 20 times, respectively, more effective than SRIF. The following report briefly discusses the potential clinical use of somatostatins.

Clinical Indications of Somatostatin

A list of potential clinical indications for somatostatins is presented in table I. Similar to the natural peptide, Sandostatin has been shown to inhibit GH secretion in man following intravenous and subcutaneous administration [2, 3] and, recently, its effectiveness in the management of acromegaly has also been demonstrated [4]. Studies conducted with Sandostatin have also reproduced the inhibitory effect of SRIF on stimulated TSH without modifying basal secretion. Only in hypothyroid subjects can a suppressive action be expected. It is interesting to note that, although SRIF has no effect on basal

Table I. Clinical uses of somatostatins

1. Central neuroendocrine disorders
   Acromegaly (hyperprolactinemia)
   Excessive TSH secretion
   Defective ACTH feedback (Addison, Nelson)
2. GI Tumors and related conditions
   Insulinoma
   Nesidioblastosis
   Vipoma
   Glucagonoma
   Gastrinoma
   Carcinoid
3. Non-tumoral GI conditions
   Malignant diarrhea
   Pancreatic fistula
   Pancreatitis
   GI bleeding
4. GI exploratory and diagnostic tool
   Examination of the upper GI tract including the exocrine pancreas, the stomach and the gallbladder
5. Diabetes
   Type I (insulinopenic)
   Type II (peripheral resistance)
6. Blood pressure regulation
   Hyperreninemia
   Aldosteronism
7. Tissue growth inhibition
   Skin (EGF?)
   Malignant tissue
8. Cytoprotection
9. Miscellaneous
   Burns, trauma, sepsis

ACTH secretion, it can inhibit its release when inadequate cortisol feedback is present such as in Nelson's syndrome and in Addison's disease.

By taking advantage of the antagonistic effect on normal and tumoral B-cell function, SRIF and Sandostatin have been used in acute trials to counteract the hypoglycemia of insulinomas or neonatal nesidioblastosis. This effect has been extended, with variable success, to other gastrointestinal tumors such as vipomas, glucagonomas, gastrinomas and the carcinoid syndrome [5].

Somatostatin has also been used in reducing excessive intestinal water excretion found in unexplained diarrhea, especially in the postnatal period. However, results in epidemic cholera have been rather disappointing. Somatostatin may find its place in the management of acute pancreatitis because of its dampening effect on pancreatic and gallbladder functions and its role in decreasing gastric acidity. Its inhibitory action on the exocrine pancreas may also assist in the control of fluid and electrolyte loss through pancreatic fistulas. These profound inhibitory effects of somatostatin on gastrointestinal function and also on gallbladder motility may in turn justify its use as a diagnostic and exploratory tool.

The effect of somatostatin on the metabolism of sugar may prove advantageous in the management of insulin-sensitive, unstable diabetes. This peptide delays intestinal absorption of glucose so that exaggerated postprandial hyperglycemia can be avoided. Its inhibitory effect on growth hormone and glucagon, two insulin antagonists, dampens counterregulatory mechanisms and thus reduces insulin requirements. Inappropriate glucose control in the early morning hours, known as the 'dawn phenomenon', may constitute another indication for long-acting somatostatin derivatives since the sleep-dependent growth hormone increase has been claimed to play a role in the etiology of this phenomenon. This subject is further documented in another contribution to this symposium.

Similar to natural somatostatin, the long-acting derivative Sandostatin reduces postural hyperreninemia without modifying aldosterone secretion in humans. The stimulating action of angiotensin II on the latter is not influenced either [6]. The effect on renin secretion, although statistically significant, is without biological relevance since doses of Sandostatin which in several studies induced profound hormonal changes, have failed to alter blood pressure.

An interesting area of potential application of somatostatin is epidermal growth and related disorders, as well as malignant tissue proliferation. The identification of growth-promoting factors has stimulated somatostatin research in this area, and the effectiveness of this peptide as an inhibitor or regulator of cellular proliferation is the subject of present investigations. In addition, severe burn injuries, a rather unusual indication, may benefit from somatostatin administration probably by mechanisms unrelated to tissue destruction and proliferation [7]. A potential indication for somatostatin may be the hormonal and metabolic disarray that follows severe trauma and sepsis. However, its role in this particular situation has not yet been established [8].

It is also interesting to mention that a 'cytoprotective' action of SRIF has been demonstrated in different models of tissue and cellular injury. This particular aspect will also be dealt with elsewhere in this symposium.

It can be concluded that somatostatin and its long-acting derivatives may prove useful in the management and diagnosis of ailments caused by excessive production of growth hormone and related growth factors, and also in conditions independent of cellular proliferation. Despite the availability of new, potent and long-acting derivatives, the multiple actions of one and the same peptide challenge biochemists and pharmacologists to synthesise and characterise derivatives with more selective action profiles.

References

1 Bauer, W.; Briner, U.; Doepfner, W.; Hall, R.; Huguenin, R.; Marbach, P.; Petcher, T.J.; Pless, J.: SMS 201-995: a very potent and selective octapeptide analogue of somatostatin with prolonged action. Life Sci. *31:* 1133–1141 (1982).

2 Pozo, E. del;Kutz, K.: Pharmacological properties and effect on glucose homeostasis of a somatostatin derivative (SMS 201-995): studies in humans; in Lüdecke, Tolis, Growth factors and acromegaly, pp. 207–214 (Raven Press, New York, 1987).

3 Pozo, E. del; Neufeld, M.; Schlüter, K.; Tortosa, F.; Clarenbach, P.; Bieder, E.; Wendel, L.; Nüesch, E.; Marbach, P.; Cramer, H.; Kerp, L.: Endocrine profile of a long-acting somatostatin derivative SMS 201-995. Study in normal volunteers following subcutaneous administration. Acta endocr., Copenh. *111:* 433–439 (1986).

4 Lamberts, S.W.J.; Uitterlinden, P.; Verschoor, L.; Dongen, K.J. van; Pozo, E. del: Long-term treatment of acromegaly with the somatostatin analogue SMS 201-995. New Engl. J. Med. *313:* 1576–1580 (1985).

5 Schrezenmeir, J.; Plewe, G.; Stürmer, W.; Kahaly, G.; Appermann, D.; Krause, U.; Pozo, E. del; Kasper, H.; Beyer, J.: Treatment of APUDomas with the long-acting somatostatin analogue SMS 201-995. Investigations of therapeutic use and digestive side effects. Scand. J. Gastroent. *21:* suppl. 119, pp. 223–227 (1986).

6 Sieber, C.; Gnädinger, M.; Pozo, E. del; Shaw, S.; Weidmann, P.: Effect of sandostatin on the renin-aldosterone axis. Clin. Endocrinol. *28:* 25–32 (1988).

7 Batstone, G.F.; Alberti, K.G.M.M.; Hinks, L.; Smythe, P.; Laing, J.E.; Ward, C.M.; Ely, D.W.; Bloom, S.R.: Metabolic studies in subjects following thermal injury. Intermediary metabolites, hormones and tissue oxygenation. Burns *2:* 207–225 (1978).

8 Frayn, K.N.: Hormonal control of metabolism in trauma and sepsis. Clin. Endocrinol. *24:* 577–599 (1986).

Dr. E. del Pozo
Sandoz Forschungsinstitut
Monbijoustrasse 115
CH-3007 Bern (Switzerland)

Hormone Res. 29: 92–94 (1988)

0301–0163/88/0293–0092$2.75/0

Effect of a Long-Acting Somatostatin Derivative SMS 201-995 (Sandostatin) on Glucose Homeostasis in Type I Diabetes mellitus

I. Navascues[a], *J. Gil*[a], *C. Pascau*[a], *D. Senén*[a], *E. del Pozo*[b], *M. Serrano-Ríos*[a]

[a]Servicio de Medicina Interna, Centro Ramón y Cajal, Madrid, España;
[b]Experimental Therapeutics Department, Clinical Research, Sandoz AG, Basle, Switzerland

Key Words. Somatostatin · Diabetes control · Counterregulation · Dawn phenomenon

Abstract. The infusion of natural somatostatin (SRIF) has been able to partially correct postprandial hyperglycemic reactions in insulin-dependent diabetes mellitus (IDDM). SMS 201-995 (Sandostatin) is a long-acting derivative with a growth hormone-suppressive effect 10–60 times more potent than the native peptide. The effect of SMS 201-995 (50 µg s.c.) on glucose control by exogenous insulin has been documented in a series of type I diabetics after stabilization of blood sugar by an artificial pancreas. Inhibition of counterregulatory mechanisms significantly diminished the postprandial hyperglycemia, and insulin requirements, both total and 2 h after meals, were markedly decreased. Also the effect of a single s.c. injection of 100 µg SMS 201-995 on the dawn phenomenon in a patient with poorly adjustable diabetes was investigated. The glucose escape observed during the control night was blocked by SMS 201-995. Thus, the stabilizing action of this peptide on postprandial and nocturnal hyperglycemia in unstable diabetes warrants further studies.

The infusion of natural somatostatin (SRIF) has been able to partially correct postprandial hyperglycemic reactions in insulin-dependent diabetes (IDDM) [1]. This favorable effect was interpreted as the result of a dual mechanism: the suppression of growth hormone and glucagon as counterregulatory hormones and a delay in glucose absorption. These actions allowed a substantial reduction in daily insulin requirements. Though promising, these favorable effects of SRIF were counterbalanced by its extremely short half-life, thus sharply reducing its potential chronic application in clinical practice. Recently, the characterization of a potent somatostatin derivative with prolonged action by Bauer et al. [2] has been followed by a series of experimental and clinical studies confirming its biological properties. This octapeptide with the code name SMS 201-995 (Sandostatin, Sandoz, Basle, Switzerland) has been found to reproduce the effect of the natural peptide on glucose homeostasis in humans. The results of clinical trials of this effect, as well as the effect of SMS 201-995 on the dawn phenomenon in a patient with brittle diabetes, are reviewed in this article.

Results of Single and Repeated Administration of SMS 201-995 in IDDM

Preliminary studies in diabetic subjects showed long-lasting inhibition of growth hormone and glucagon secretion and dampening of glucose oscillations after intravenous or subcutaneous administration of SMS 201-995. The postprandial glucose rise was reduced considerably and the peak concentration was delayed. The latter was interpreted as the result of slow sugar uptake from the gut. Previous *D*-xylose absorption studies in normal volunteers have clearly shown blunting of the plasma profile of this pentose by SMS 201-995, but the area covered by the curve was not different from a placebo control reflecting retarded absorption [3]. In general, subcutaneous administration of 50 or 100 µg was sufficient to produce this effect which was maintained for about 6 h. In some instances, there was a tendency towards hypoglycemic reactions in the evening hours. Therefore, a 30–50% insulin dose reduction before sleep is recommended if a low blood sugar has already been recorded during the diurnal trial. This subject has been discussed in a recent review [4].

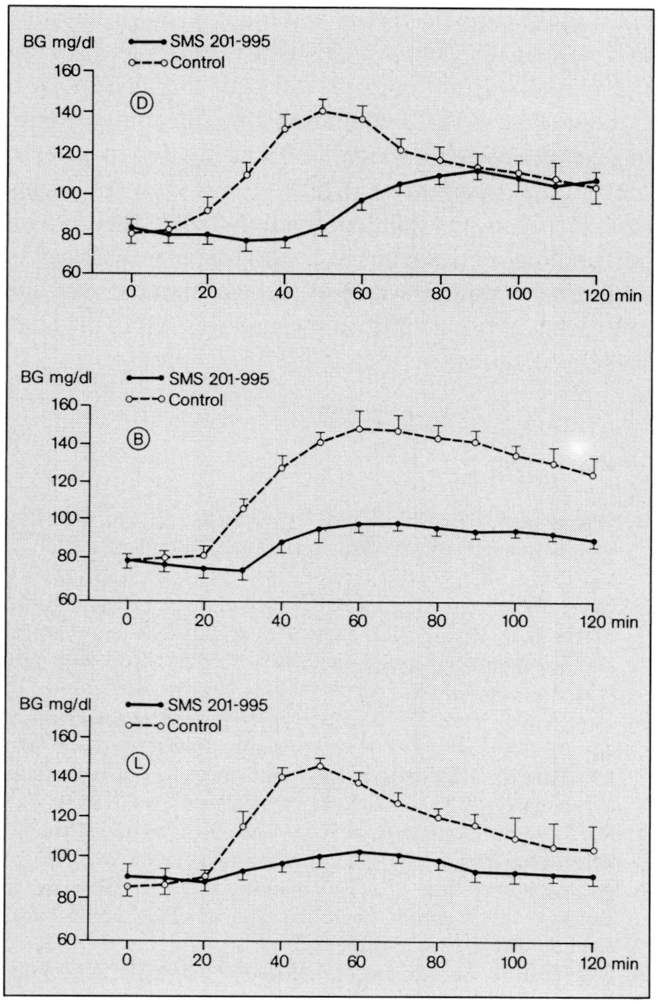

1

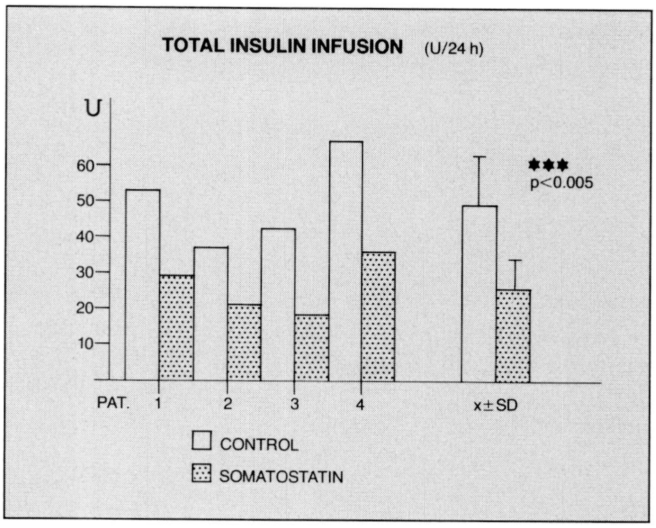

2

Fig. 1. Prostprandial blood glucose profiles recorded in 6 subjects with type I diabetes mellitus after stabilisation with a Biostator. Sandostatin (SMS 201–995) markedly reduced the glycemic peaks following a standard mixed meal.

Fig. 2. Insulin saving effect recorded in 4 unstable diabetics after adjustment with a Biostator and administration of Sandostatin, 50 μg t.i.d. The cumulative insulin dose for 24 hours is shown.

The effect of SMS 201-995 on glucose control by exogenous insulin has been documented in a series of type I diabetics after stabilization of blood sugar by an artificial pancreas [5]. Standardized mixed meals were ingested following a subcutaneous injection of 50 μg SMS 201-995. The resulting inhibition of counterregulatory mechanisms significantly diminished the postprandial hyperglycemia (fig. 1). Insulin requirements, both total and 2 h after meals, were also markedly decreased (fig. 2). This was accompanied by a substantial fall in circulating glucagon. Recurrent or persistent hyperglycemia and induced hyperinsulinemia have been claimed to play a role in the etiology of diabetic vascular complications. Thus, the effect of SMS 201-995 on counterregulatory mechanisms may be advantageous to the better management of patients with propensity to metabolic instability, and may represent a potential tool for the prevention of complications of the disease.

Effect of SMS 201-995 on the Dawn Phenomenon

Although a detailed analysis of this subject is beyond the scope of this presentation, some remarks about the dominant role of growth hormone (GH) in the development of early morning hyperglycemia in diabetes are pertinent. This issue is still controversial despite a body of evidence showing correspondence between the sleep GH peak and changes in blood sugar [6]. The so-called dawn phenomenon can also be observed in nondiabetic subjects but hyperglycemia can be readily controlled by mobilization of pancreatic insulin reserve.

The effect of a single subcutaneous injection of 100 μg SMS 201-995 on the dawn phenomenon in a patient with poorly adjustable diabetes is illustrated in figure 3. During two EEG-monitored sleep periods the subject received a subcutaneous injection of either a placebo or 50 μg SMS 201-995 at midnight. Subsequently,

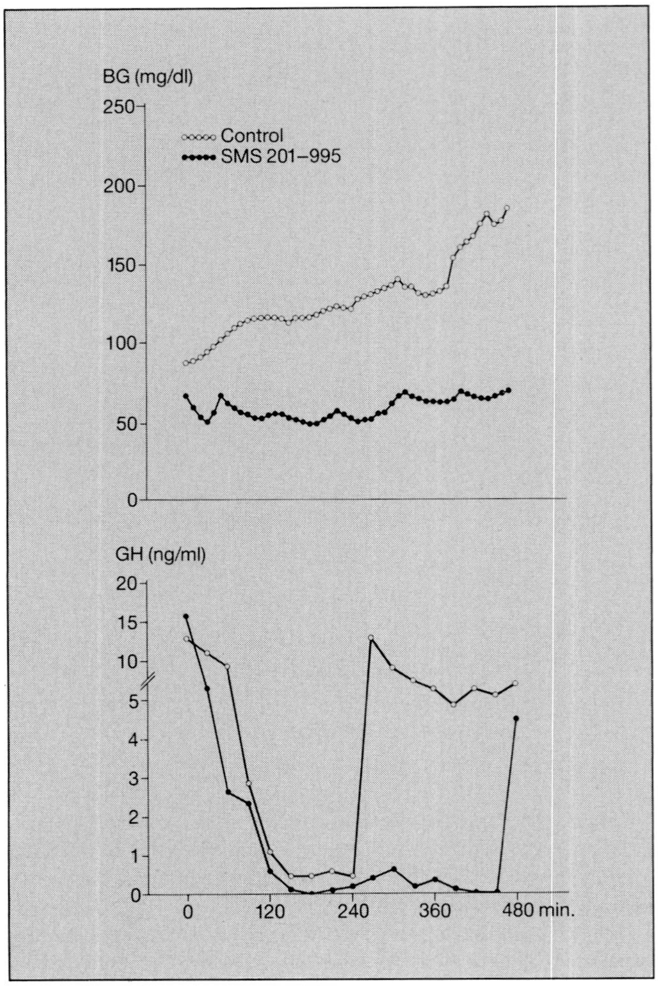

Fig. 3. Nocturnal blood glucose and GH profiles in a diabetic subject under continuous insulin infusion (0.15 mU/kg/min). The glucose escape recorded during the morning hours is blocked by Sandostatin (black dots) and GH is suppressed throughout this period.

0.15 mU/kg/min doses of regular insulin were infused covering an observation period of 8 h. Figure 3 clearly shows the difference between basal and treatment periods. Despite continuous insulin infusion there is a glucose escape which builds up gradually reaching maximum levels at 8 a.m. (480 min). In contrast, glucose values remain stable between 50 and 70 mg% after SMS 201-995 injection. In this trial, the GH peak expected to occur in the early sleep stage was missing. It is interesting to note that the glucose increment recorded in the control period was not coincidental with the physiological GH surge. Also the potentiating effect of somatostatin, in general, on insulin should be borne in mind in order to prevent the occurrence of hypoglycemic episodes during sleep [1]. Thus, the stabilizing action of SMS 201-995 on postprandial and nocturnal hyperglycemia observed in preliminary studies warrants the continuation of the evaluation of this peptide in the management of unstable diabetes mellitus.

References

1 Gottesmann, I.S.; Mandarino, I.J.; Gerich, J.E.: Somatostatin: its role in health and disease. Spec. Top. Endocrinol. Metab. *4:* 177–243 (1982).
2 Bauer, W.; Briner, U.; Doepfner, W.; Hall, R.; Huguenin, R.; Marbach, P.; Petcher, T.J.; Pless, J.: SMS 201-995: a very potent and selective octapeptide analogue of somatostatin with prolonged action. Life Sci. *31:* 1133–1141 (1982).
3 Pozo, E. del; Kutz, K.: Pharmacological properties and effect on glucose homeostasis of a somatostatin derivative (SMS 201-995): studies in humans; in Lüdecke, Tolis, Growth factors and acromegaly, pp. 207–214 (Raven Press, New York, 1987).
4 Pozo, E. del; Lamberts, S.W.J.; Sieber, C.; Gomez-Pan, A.: Effect of a long-acting somatostatin analog (SMS 201-995) on glucose homeostasis in type I diabetes and in acromegaly; in Reichlin, Somatostatin, basic and clinical status, pp. 293–302 (Plenum Press, New York, 1987).
5 Serrano-Rios, M.; Navascues, I.; Saban, J.; Ordoñez, A.; Sevilla, F.; del Pozo, E.: Somatostatin analog SMS 201-995 and insulin needs in insulin-dependent diabetic patients studied by means of an artificial pancreas. J. clin. Endocr. Metab. *53:* 675–681 (1987).
6 Campbell, P.; Bolli, G.; Cryer, P.; Gerich, J.: Pathogenesis of the dawn phenomenon in patients with insulin-dependent diabetes mellitus. N. Engl. J. Med. *312:* 1473–1479 (1985).

Dr. I. Navascues
Servicio de Medicina Interna
Centro Ramon y Cajal
Madrid (Spain)

Hormone Res. 29: 95–98 (1988)

0301–0163/88/0293–0095$2.75/0

Preliminary Experience on Treatment of Insulin-Dependent Diabetes mellitus with a Long-Acting Somatostatin Analogue (L363,586)

G.B. Bolli [a], *I.S. Gottesman* [b], *J.E. Gerich* [c]

[a] Istituto di Patologia Medica, Università di Perugia, Italia; [b] Mount Sinai Hospital, Toronto, Ont., Canada;
[c] Clinical Research Center, Section of Diabetes, University of Pittsburgh, Pa., USA

Key Words. Somatostatin · Intravenous · Intranasal · Dawn phenomenon

Abstract. L363,586 is a potent, long-acting, somatostatin derivative. Intravenous and intranasal administration to diabetic subjects was effective in reducing both fasting and postprandial hyperglycemia. Also in patients stabilized on a closed-loop insulin infusion device, the intranasal administration of L363,586 was able to improve the glucose imbalance known as dawn phenomenon. Therefore, this analogue associated to standard insulin replacement could be useful in the control of unstable diabetes.

The ability of acute infusions of somatostatin to decrease fasting [1] and postprandial [2] hyperglycemia in human diabetes, and to prevent the development of severe ketoacidosis following acute insulin withdrawal from insulin-dependent diabetes [3], has suggested that somatostatin or some longer-acting and more selective analogues may be useful as an adjunct to insulin in the management of metabolic derangement in diabetes mellitus. However, the short biologic half-life of somatostatin and its wide range of biological actions make the use of somatostatin impractical as a therapeutic agent. In order to circumvent some of these limitations, attempts have been made to produce analogues that are longer acting and more selective.

L363,586 (now referred to as MK-678) is a cyclic hexapeptide analogue of somatostatin. This compound was developed by chemists at Merck, Sharp & Dohme Research Laboratories on the basis of modelling of the active site of the somatostatin molecule in a project which involved the synthesis of more than 150 analogues [4]. The amino acid sequence of MK-678 is: Cyclo(N-Me-Ala-Tye-*D*-Trp-Lys-Val-Phe).

Based on its prolonged duration of action and potency of more than 50 times that of somatostatin in animal and in vitro studies [4], L363,586 was chosen to undergo evaluation in patients with insulin-dependent diabetes mellitus (IDDM). Initial studies were therefore undertaken to assess its metabolic clearance rate and half-life during 5-hour intravenous infusions, as well as its concomitant effect on postprandial plasma glucose, glucagon, growth hormone and triglyceride levels.

Acute and Continuous Intravenous Administration of L363,586

Three doses (2.5, 10 and 40 μg/h) of L363,586 were compared with placebo and a 200 μg/h somatostatin infusion. Xylose (5 g) was incorporated into the standard test meal given to 6 patients with IDDM to assess the effect of the analogue on carbohydrate absorption. The subjects had been withdrawn from their intermediate-acting (lente or NPH) insulin at least 24 h prior to entering the Clinical Study Unit. During this period they were managed on multiple subcutaneous injections of regular insulin (Iletin II, Eli Lilly, Indianapolis, Ind.). After receiving a standard supper, the subjects were connected to a closed-loop insulin infusion device (GCIIS, Biostator®, Life Science Instruments, Elkhart, Ind.) and were maintained euglycemic with it overnight. The following morning, subjects received a standard injection of regular insulin (Iletin II, 0.15 U/kg) 30 min prior to beginning breakfast which was consumed over 15 min. Infusions of L363,586, somatostatin or placebo were begun

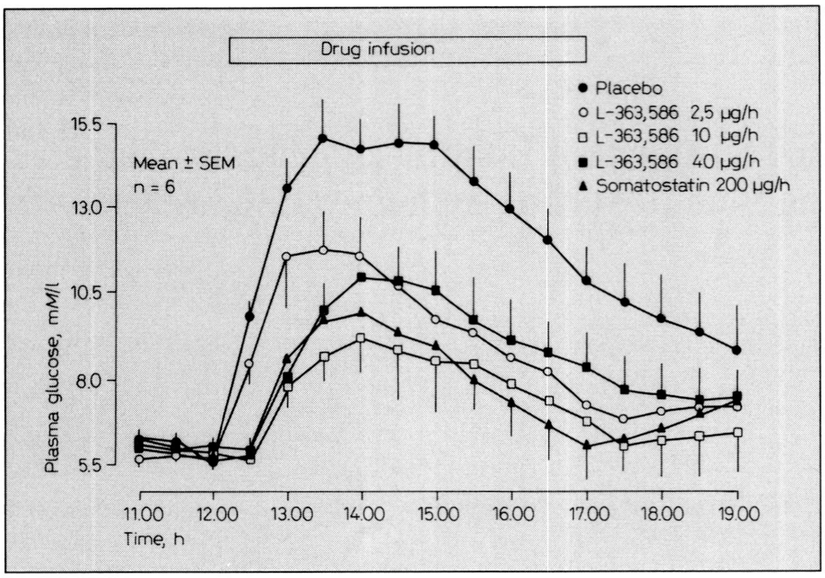

Fig. 1. Effect of L363,586 on postprandial plasma glucose levels in IDDM patients (explanation in text).

at the time of meal ingestion. Levels during the 2.5 µg/h infusion were too low to reliably calculate a half-life, but from values obtained during the other two infusions, the metabolic clearance rate was approximately 300 ml/min and the half-life was 45 min.

Plasma glucagon and growth hormone were suppressed to a comparable extent with all three doses of L363,586 and somatostatin, but after termination of the intravenous somatostatin infusion, a rebound increase in plasma concentrations of the hormones was observed, whereas none occurred during the infusion of L363,586.

Postprandial plasma glucose levels in the diabetic subjects (fig. 1) were significantly reduced with all three doses of L363,586 and with somatostatin. L363,586 infused at 10 µg/h was as effective as somatostatin infused at a rate of 200 µg/h, producing approximately a 70% reduction in the area under the postprandial plasma glucose curve (67 ± 23 vs. 224 ± 22 m*M*/l/5 h with placebo, $p < 0.01$).

The diminution of postprandial hyperglycemia by L363,586 does not appear to be wholly explicable on the basis of a delaying of carbohydrate absorption since there has been a dissociation between reduction in postprandial plasma xylose responses and the reduction in postprandial hyperglycemia. Thus, the 10-µg/h infusion of L363,586 that had produced a maximal (~70%) reduction in postprandial hyperglycemia produced only a 25% reduction in postprandial plasma xylose responses (9.5 ± 0.7 vs. 12.9 ± 0.5 m*M*/l/5 h with placebo, $p < 0.05$). A maximal reduction of only 35% was seen with the 40-µg/h L363,586 and 200-µg/h somatostatin infusions. Accordingly, these results provide indirect support of a role for excessive meal-stimulated glucagon secretion in the pathogenesis of postprandial hyperglycemia in IDDM patients [2].

Following these encouraging acute results, further experiments were undertaken examining the effect of a 3-day continuous infusion of L363,586 at a rate of 0.5 µg/h in 8 volunteers with IDDM. Twenty-four-hour profiles of plasma glucose, glucagon, growth hormone and free insulin were determined on the third day of L363,586 and placebo infusions. In addition, stools were collected for determination of fat content. Without a change in insulin dose, there was a 32% decrease in mean 24-hour plasma glucose concentration (212 ± 21 vs. 145 ± 11 mg/dl, $p < 0.005$). This occurred despite only modest reductions in 24-hour plasma glucagon and growth hormone levels (about 15 and 20%, respectively, both $p < 0.05$). Three-day stool fat increased in 6 of the 8 subjects from 5.3 ± 0.5 to 7.4 ± 1.9 g/day but this was not statistically significant.

The analogue was well tolerated with no adverse signs or symptoms except transient mild dyspepsia and increased frequency of loose stools.

Intranasal Administration of L363,586

Since injections of L363,586 taken in addition to insulin might dissuade use of this analogue, our next set of experiments were undertaken to determine whether

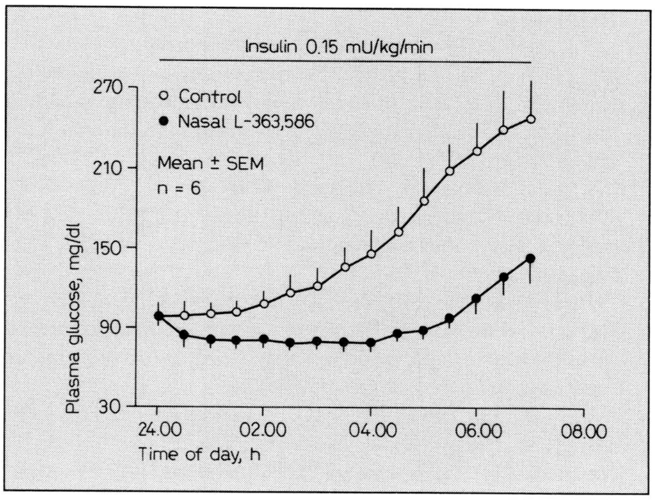

Fig. 2. Effect of intranasal L363,586 on development of early morning hyperglycemia (dawn phenomenon) in IDDM patients.

the nasal route of administration was feasible, safe and effective.

Six subjects with IDDM were given 25, 100 and 400 µg of L363,586 by intranasal droplet 0.5 h before a standard breakfast and supper with a standard lunch being taken in between. Subjects were admitted to the Clinical Study Unit the night before experiments after having been withdrawn from their intermediate-acting insulin and treated with multiple subcutaneous injections of regular insulin for at least 24 h. They were given a standard supper and connected to a closed-loop insulin infusion device (Biostator GCIIS, Life Science Instruments, Elkhart, Ind.), which maintained them euglycemic overnight. A mixture of regular and lente insulin was given 0.5 h before breakfast.

The 25-µg dose produced no discernible effects on any of the parameters measured. With the 100- and 400-µg doses, plasma glucose levels through the day were lower than those observed after placebo and the 25-µg dose. Both the 100- and 400-µg doses reduced postprandial plasma glucose concentrations by 40–50% and completely prevented any increases in plasma triglycerides, glucagon and growth hormone. Plasma xylose concentrations were not affected by the 25-µg dose and were reduced comparably (~25%) with the 100- and 400-µg doses.

Thus, these studies showed that 100 µg L363,586 taken intranasally lasted at least 6 h and therefore could be used on a twice daily basis to aid in the control of postprandial hyperglycemia in patients with IDDM. In general, the nasal route was well tolerated with only one subject complaining of transient nasal irritation, but this was also observed with placebo. Loose bowel movement occurred in 4 subjects after the 100-µg dose and in 5 after the 400-µg dose. These episodes occurred between 8 and 18 h after the second dose of the peptide.

Plasma levels of L363,586 after intranasal administration were reached within 1 h, the first sampling time. The initial decrease in levels had a half-life of about 45 min, similar to that observed with intravenous infusion.

Effect of L363,586 on the Dawn Phenomenon

Since the intranasal administration appeared to be a feasible route of delivery for L363,586, we examined its effect on the dawn phenomenon when given by this route at bedtime. The dawn phenomenon is an early morning increase in insulin requirements occurring in patients with either IDDM or non-IDDM [5] as well as in non-diabetic individuals [6].

Current evidence [7] indicates that nocturnal surges in growth hormone are the cause. In patients with diabetes mellitus due to the inability to secrete additional insulin to compensate for the growth hormone-induced insulin resistance, marked hyperglycemia can develop in the early morning.

One of the major problems in managing the dawn phenomenon is its variability which is presumably due to erratic growth hormone secretion. Production of consistent suppression of overnight growth hormone secretion should reduce this variability and make it easier to determine overnight insulin doses.

Therefore, to test the feasibility of treating the dawn phenomenon with a long-acting somatostatin analogue like L363,586, six volunteers with IDDM, who had been withdrawn from their intermediate-acting insulin for 24 h and managed solely by subcutaneous injections of regular insulin, were placed on a closed-loop insulin infusion device, rendered euglycemic after a standard supper and were infused with insulin at a constant rate from midnight to 7 a.m. on two occasions. On one occasion they received intranasal L363,586 (600 µg) and on the other, saline. Intranasal administration of L363,586 completely suppressed nocturnal surges in growth hormone secretion and reduced plasma glucagon levels throughout the night. Plasma cortisol and free insulin levels were not affected. As shown in figure 2, in control experiments, plasma glucose increased to over 250 mg/dl, whereas when L363,586 was administered plasma glucose did not increase until after 5 a.m. and then only to less than 150 g/dl. This increase presumably was due to the progressive decreases in plasma free insulin resulting from reduced delivery of insulin with the Biostator [8]. None of the subjects experienced untoward effects from the intranasal L363,586. These studies therefore indicate that such administration of a long-acting analogue might be feasible for managing the dawn phenomenon in patients in whom this cannot be done safely and effectively with mere adjustments in insulin doses.

In conclusion, in acute and relatively short-term studies, L363,586 was well tolerated when given by both intravenous and intranasal routes and was also effective in reducing both fasting and postprandial hyperglycemia in patients with IDDM. Its main side effect was steatorrhea. Such an agent might prove to be useful as an adjunct to insulin in the treatment of diabetes mellitus especially in patients unwilling or unable to take more than two daily injections of insulin and in whom maintenance of near-normoglycemia is a therapeutic goal. However, long-term studies are needed to establish the feasibility, safety and effectiveness of such a therapeutic approach in IDDM.

Acknowledgements

The editorial assistance of Patricia Boyce is gratefully acknowledged. This work was supported by the Consiglio Nazionale delle Ricerche (CNR finalized project, Complications of diabetes, Ob-46; and CNR grant 86.00021.04).

References

1 Del Guercio, M.; Di Natale, B.; Gargantini, L.; Garlaschi, C.; Chiumello, G.: Effect of somatostatin on blood sugar, plasma growth hormone, and glucagon levels in diabetic children. Diabetes *25:* 550–553 (1976).

2 Gerich, J.; Lorenzi, M.; Karam, J.; Schneider, V.; Forsham, P.: Abnormal pancreatic glucagon secretion and postprandial hyperglycaemia in diabetes mellitus. J. Am. med. Ass. *234:* 159–165 (1975).

3 Gerich, J.; Lorenzi, M.; Bier, D.; Schneider, V.; Tsalikian, E.; Karam, J.; Forsham, P.: Prevention of human diabetic ketoacidosis by somatostatin: evidence for an essential role of glucagon. New Engl. J. Med. *292:* 985–989 (1975).

4 Veber, D.; Saperstein, R.; Nutt, T.; Freidinger, R.; Brady, S.; Curley, P.; Perlow, D.; Paleveda, W.; Zacchei, A.; Tocco, D.; Vandlen, R.; Gerich, J.; Hall, L.; Mandarino, L.; Cordes, E.; Anderson, P.; Hirschmann, R.: A superactive cyclic hexapeptide analogue of somatostatin. Life Sci. *35:* 1371–1378 (1984).

5 Bolli, G.; Gerich, J.: The dawn phenomenon. A common occurrence in both noninsulin-dependent and insulin-dependent diabetes mellitus. New Engl. J. Med. *310:* 746–750 (1984).

6 Bolli, G.; De Feo, P.; De Cosmo, S.; Perriello, G.; Ventura, M.; Calcinaro, F.; Lolli, C.; Compagnucci, P.; Campbell, P.; Brunetti, P.; Gerich, J.: Demonstration of a dawn phenomenon in normal human volunteers. Diabetes *33:* 1150–1153 (1984).

7 Campbell, P.; Bolli, G.; Cryer, P.; Gerich, J.: Pathogenesis of the dawn phenomenon in patients with insulin-dependent diabetes mellitus. New Engl. J. Med. *312:* 1473–1479 (1985).

8 Brennan, J.; Gebhart, S.; Blackard, W.: Pump-induced insulin aggregation. A problem with the Biostator. Diabetes *34:* 353–359 (1985).

Dr. G.B. Bolli
Istituto di Patologia Medica dell'Università
Via E. Dal Pozzo
I–06100 Perugia (Italy)

Hormone Res. *29:* 99–102 (1988)

0301–0163/88/0293–0099$2.75/0

Effects of Somatostatin in Patients with Portal Hypertension

Jaume Bosch, David Kravetz, Ricardo Mastai, Miquel Navasa, Guillermo Silva, Jaime Chesta, Juan Rodes

Hepatic Haemodynamics Laboratory, Liver Unit, Hospital Clinic i Provincial, University of Barcelona, Spain

Key Words. Somatostatin · Liver disease · Portal hypertension

Abstract. Portal hypertension is a common complication of chronic liver disease. Conventional therapy consists of surgery and palliative measures for the hemodynamic problem. It has been recently reported that somatostatin may reduce portal pressure without altering the systemic circulation and so reducing hepatic blood flow. This peptide also causes a significant fall in azygos circulation in patients with esophageal varices. The mechanism of this effect is unclear although suppression of intestinal vasodilating hormones and of glucagon have been claimed to play a role. Comparative clinical studies have shown somatostatin to be superior to the standard vasopressin treatment. Recent findings suggest that the efficacy of somatostatin can be increased by administering this peptide in repeated intravenous bolus injections. New derivatives, specially long-acting peptides, may eventually prove beneficial in the chronic treatment of this complication.

Introduction

Portal hypertension is a common syndrome, most frequently caused by chronic liver disease, which is characterized by a pathological increase of portal venous pressure and by the formation of a network of portosystemic collaterals that include esophageal and gastric varices. These are responsible for the main complication of portal hypertension, massive gastrointestinal bleeding from ruptured varices, which constitutes one of the leading causes of death in patients with cirrhosis of the liver [1–3].

Therapy of portal hypertension has been based on surgery and on different instrumental procedures. Recently, increasing interest has been paid to the possibilities of pharmacological treatment of portal hypertension [1, 4]. This is based on the concept that since portal pressure is the result of the product of blood flow and vascular resistance within the portal venous system, any drug that might reduce the portal blood flow (for instance, causing splanchnic vasoconstriction) will also reduce portal pressure [4]. It is conceivable that reduction of pressure and blood flow within the portal system and esophageal varices will be helpful to arrest and prevent variceal hemorrhage [4].

Until very recently, vasopressin was the only drug used in the pharmacological treatment of portal hypertension. However, the many adverse cardiovascular effects of vasopressin make it a dangerous agent [1]. Because of this, the demonstration that in patients with cirrhosis of the liver, somatostatin administration allows portal pressure to be reduced without altering the systemic circulation [1], suggested that it can become a useful agent in the treatment of portal hypertension. This paper will review the hemodynamic and clinical experience accumulated with the use of somatostatin in portal hypertension in recent years.

Hemodynamic Effects of Somatostatin

Portal Pressure

Recent investigations have demonstrated a rapid decline in portal pressure following somatostatin injection [1, 4]. Subsequent investigations confirmed these find-

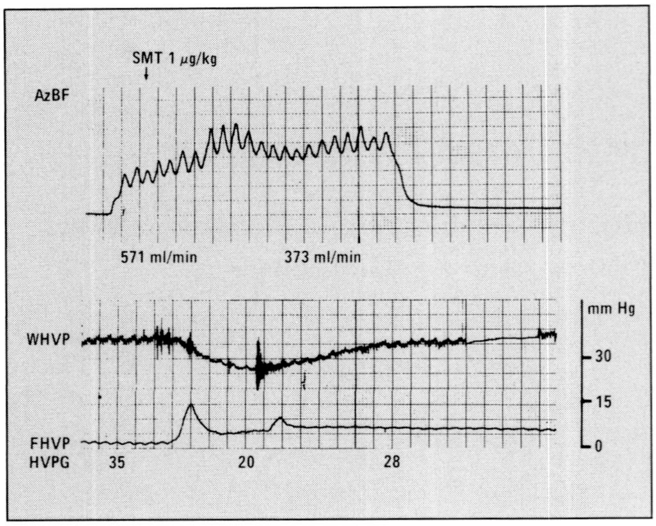

Fig. 1. Effects of a bolus injection of somatostatin (arrow) on azygous blood flow (AzBF), wedged hepatic venous pressure (WHVP), free hepatic venous pressure (FHVP), and on the hepatic venous pressure gradient (HVPG) in a patient with cirrhosis and sinusoidal portal hypertension. Notice the rapid and transient decline in azygous blood flow and portal pressure (HVPG), due to both a fall in WHVP and to an increase in FHVP. [Reproduced with permission from Clin. Gastroenterol. *14:* 169 (1985).]

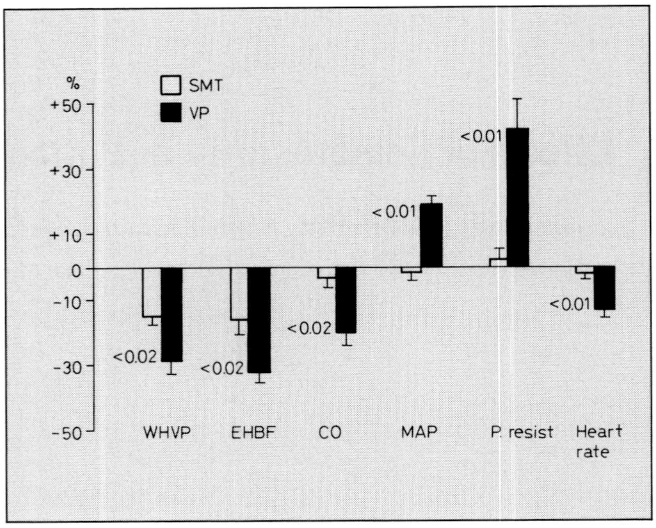

Fig. 2. Comparison of the effects of a continuous infusion of somatostatin (SMT, 7.5 μg/min preceded by a bolus of 70 μg) and vasopressin (VP, 0.4 U/min) on the corrected WHVP, hepatic blood flow (EHBF), cardiac output (CO), mean arterial pressure (MAP), peripheral vascular resistance (P. resist) and heart rate in patients with cirrhosis. Data are presented as percent change from baseline. [Reproduced with permission from Gastroenterology *80:* 518–525 (1981).]

ings and showed that while portal pressure is markedly reduced by bolus injections of somatostatin (fig. 1), this effect is transient, and usually disappears in 1–2 min [4, 6], which may be related to the very short plasma half-life of natural somatostatin. The effect of continuous intravenous infusions is much less, averaging 10–17% with infusion of 7.5 μg/min [1]. Some investigations using lower rates (2.5 μg/min) failed to document significant effects of somatostatin on portal pressure [7]. It appears that there is no tachyphylaxis to the portal pressure-reducing effect of somatostatin [6]. There is still not enough information on the effects of the new, long-acting somatostatin analogs in this particular situation.

Hepatic and Portal Venous Blood Flow

Somatostatin infusion reduces the hepatic blood flow in normal man [7] and in patients with cirrhosis [1, 6]. This is due to vasoconstriction of the splanchnic arteries. Decrease in portal blood flow is the main determinant of the fall in hepatic irrigation [1]. Reduction in portal blood flow is causally related to the fall in portal pressure, since the compound lacks any effect on hepatic vascular resistance. However, the exact mechanism by which somatostatin modifies hepatic flow is poorly understood. Experimental studies suggest that it may actually increase portal venous resistance, either because of passive collapse of the vessels secondary to the fall in portal blood flow, or because of a hypothetical venoconstrictor effect [4]. The action of somatostatin infusions on portal pressure and blood flow is significantly lesser than that of standard vasopressin treatment (fig. 2) [1, 5–7]. It has been recently proposed that increased circulating levels of glucagon, which is markedly suppressed by somatostatin, may be an important determinant of the splanchnic vasodilation associated to chronic portal hypertension.

Azygous Blood Flow

Measurement of azygous venous blood flow by continuous thermal dilution is a recently introduced technique that allows one to estimate blood flow changes at the gastroesophageal collaterals and esophageal varices draining into the azygous vein [8]. Recent studies have shown that somatostatin causes a significant reduction in azygous blood flow in patients with esophageal varices [6, 8], reflecting a decrease in the esophageal collateral blood flow. This beneficial effect is much greater following bolus injections than with continuous i.v. infusion [6], which suggests that bolus injections are of greater

Table I. Controlled studies comparing somatostatin and vasopressin infusions in the treatment of variceal hemorrhage

	Kravetz et al. [2]	Jenkins et al. [3]
Duration of therapy, h	48	18–24
Control of bleeding at 24 h		
Somatostatin	26/30 (87%)	10/10 (100%)
Vasopressin	23/31 (74%)	4/12 (33%)*
Control of bleeding at 48 h		
Somatostatin	16/30 (53%)	–
Vasopressin	18/31 (58%)	–
Major complications[1]		
Somatostatin	0/30	0/10
Vasopressin	8/31 (26%)*	2/12 (17%)
Minor complications		
Somatostatin	3/30 (10%)	–
Vasopressin	15/31 (48%)*	–
Mortality		
Somatostatin	14/30 (47%)	2/10 (20%)
Vasopressin	14/31 (45%)	4/12 (33%)

* $p < 0.05$ vs. somatostatin.
[1] Requiring discontinuation of therapy.

therapeutic potential, provided that its effect can be sustained (i.e. by giving repeated injections at short intervals).

Systemic Hemodynamics

The main advantage of somatostatin over vasopressin infusion is that it lacks the adverse effects of vasopressin on the systemic circulation. As shown in figure 2, neither the cardiac output, nor the heart rate, systemic vascular resistance and mean arterial pressure are significantly modified by somatostatin infusion, while the contrary is observed during vasopressin administration [1, 5]. This preferential effect of somatostatin on the splanchnic circulation is also noticed after bolus injections, although in this case these are accompanied by transient systemic effects, such as a reduction in heart rate and cardiac output, and a rise in mean arterial blood pressure [4, 6].

Use of Somatostatin in Acute Variceal Bleeding

The use of somatostatin in the treatment of acute variceal bleeding has been assessed in a surprisingly small number of controlled, randomized investigations. Only two studies have been published so far [2, 3], both comparing the effectiveness and complications of somatostatin and vasopressin infusions (table I). As shown in table I, in both studies somatostatin appeared to allow a high rate of control of bleeding during the first day of therapy. Although in the study by Jenkins et al. [3] somatostatin was significantly better than vasopressin, this was not confirmed in another investigation by Kravetz et al. [2], including a much larger number of patients who received comparable doses of the drug. It is worth remarking that despite this high initial success rate, a relatively large number of patients rebled during therapy, so that only in about half of them was the hemorrhage completely controlled, a number which does not differ from that observed with vasopressin [4].

Unfortunately, there is no study comparing somatostatin to a placebo, which is the only way to objectively assess the efficacy of somatostatin in variceal bleeding. This is especially important since a recent study suggested that vasopressin is not superior to a placebo in these patients [9]. However, as summarized in table I, somatostatin appears to be much safer than vasopressin, as evidenced by a significantly lower number of complications related to therapy in both studies [2, 3]. Although vasopressin causes major complications in a relatively high number of patients (17–26%), this does not appear to markedly influence the outcome, as suggested by the similar mortality rates in both treatment groups in the two studies.

As discussed above, recent work from our laboratory suggests that the efficacy of somatostatin might be increased by administering repeated bolus injections, given at frequent intervals (i.e. 50–100 µg every 15–20 min) during the first few hours [6]. A continuous infusion would be maintained afterwards only when the bleeding has been controlled. This is based on the observation that the hemodynamic effects of somatostatin on portal pressure and azygous blood flow are much greater following bolus injections than during continuous i.v. infusions, and that there is no tachyphylaxis after repeated administration of somatostatin [6]. It is likely that if bleeding is not stopped when the drug is exerting maximal effects, it will not cease later on when somatostatin will only cause a mild reduction in portal pressure. However, it is unknown whether an optimized method of somatostatin administration will favorably compare to the current vasopressin therapy. It has recently been proved that the association of i.v. sublingual nitroglycerin to vasopressin infusion increases the efficacy and reduces the complications of this therapy [5, 10, 11]. Association of somatostatin to more conventional therapy may be helpful in the management of complications caused by increased portal hypertension.

Acknowledgments

This work was supported by the Comision Asesora para la Investigacion Cientifica y Tecnica (1853/83–85) and the Fundacio Catalana per a l'Estudi de les Malaties del Fetge. The authors are indebted to Mrs. M. Angels Baringo for her expert technical assistance.

References

1 Bosch, J.; Kravetz, D.; Rodes, J.: Effects of somatostatin on hepatic and systemic haemodynamics in patients with cirrhosis. Gastroenterology *80:* 518–525 (1981).
2 Kravetz, D.; Bosch, J.; Teres, J.; Bruix, J.; Rimola, A.; Rodes, J.: Comparison of somatostatin and vasopressin infusions in treatment of acute variceal hemorrhage. Hepatology *4:* 442–446 (1984).
3 Jenkins, S.A.; Baxter, J.N.; Corbett, W.; Devitt, P.; Ware, J.; Shields, R.: A prospective randomised controlled clinical trial comparing somatostatin and vasopressin in controlling acute variceal haemorrhage. Br. med. J. *290:* 275–278 (1985).
4 Bosch, J.: Effects of pharmacological agents on portal hypertension. Clin. Gastroenterol. *14:* 169–184 (1985).
5 Grossmann, R.J.; Kravetz, D.; Bosch, J.; Glickman, M.; Bruix, J.; Bredfeldt, J.; Conn, H.O.; Rodes, J.: Storer, E.H.: Nitroglycerin improves the hemodynamic response to vasopressin in portal hypertension. Hepatology *2:* 757–762 (1982).
6 Mastai, R.; Bosch, J.; Navasa, M.; Silva, G.; Kravetz, D.; Bruix, J.; Viola, C.; Rodes, J.: Effect of continuous infusion and bolus injection of somatostatin on azygos blood flow and hepatic and systemic haemodynamics in patients with portal hypertension. J. Hepatol. *3:* suppl. 1, p. S53 (1986).
7 Eriksson, L.S.; Law, D.H.; Sato, Y.; Wahren, J.: Influence of somatostatin on splanchnic haemodynamics in patients with liver cirrhosis. Clin. Physiol. *4:* 5–11 (1984).
8 Bosch, J.; Mastai, R.; Kravetz, D.; Bruix, J.; Rigau, J.; Rodes, J.: Measurement of azygos venous blood flow in the evaluation of portal hypertension in patients with cirrhosis of the liver. J. Hepatol. *1:* 125–139 (1985).
9 Fogel, M.R.; Knauer, C.M.; Andres, L.L.; Mahal, A.S.; Stein, D.E.; Kemeny, M.J.; Rinki, M.M.; Walker, J.E.; Siegmund, D.; Gregory, P.B.: Continuous intravenous vasopressin in active upper gastrointestinal bleeding. Ann. intern. Med. *96:* 565–569 (1982).
10 Gimson, A.E.; Westaby, D.; Hegarty, J.; Watson, A.; Roger, W.: A randomized trial of vasopressin and vasopressin plus nitroglycerin in the control of acute variceal hemorrhage. Hepatology *6:* 410–413 (1986).
11 Tsai, Y.T.; Lay, C.S.; Lay, K.H.; Ng, W.W.; Yeh, Y.S.; Wang, J.Y.; Chiang, T.T.; Lee, S.D.; Chian, B.N.; Lo, K.J.: Controlled trial of vasopressin plus nitroglycerin vs. vasopressin alone in the treatment of bleeding esophageal varices. Hepatology *6:* 406–409 (1986).

Dr. Jaume Bosch
Hepatic Haemodynamics Laboratory
Liver Unit
Hospital Clinic i Provincial
University of Barcelona
Barcelona (Spain)

Hormone Res. *29:* 103–105 (1988)

0301–0163/88/0293–0103$2.75/0

Somatostatin in the Management of Gastrointestinal Hemorrhage: Bleeding Ulcers

J.L. Balibrea, A.J. Torres, F.H. Merlo, A. Suarez, R.F. Lobato, R. Cuberes

Department of Surgery, San Carlos University Hospital, University of Madrid, Spain

Key Words. Somatostatin · Peptic ulcers · Gastrointestinal hemorrhage

Abstract. Stress ulcers are characterized by difficult management and poor prognosis. They currently represent a complication in the clinical course of other conditions, mainly shock states. The pathogenesis of stress ulcers is not well understood although the role of hypovolemia leading to energetic deprivation and instauration of anaerobic cellular metabolism have been carefully studied. Somatostatin has been found to reduce the incidence of experimental stress ulcers. In the clinic, patients with duodenal ulcers were found to exhibit a low number of antral D cells and a significant decrease in tissue somatostatin. In a multicenter trial, patients with bleeding peptic or stress ulcers were treated with somatostatin or cimetidine plus pirenzepine. Results were favorable to the former substance on account of the time required to stop the hemorrhage and the demands for blood replacement. Thus, medical management of bleeding ulcers with somatostatin may represent an alternative to more radical surgical intervention.

Introduction

Upper gastrointestinal bleeding represents a major problem in emergency surgery; overall mortality in patients with severe bleeding has not changed in spite of great advances in resuscitation techniques, diagnostic aids and surgery [1]. The most important causes are peptic ulcer, esophageal varices and gastric carcinoma; however, in the last years, special attention has been paid to the nosologic entity described as diffuse gastroduodenal hemorrhagic ulcerative lesions, hemorrhagic gastritis or stress ulcers. The prognosis of patients with this condition is very poor, because it represents a complication in the clinical course of other systemic diseases, such as shock states.

Stress ulcer is not well understood in its pathogenic mechanisms, and sometimes the therapeutic approach is mistaken, especially when surgical intervention is indicated and methods based on the pathogenesis of peptic ulcer (i.e. vagotomy) are carried out; in clinical practice, these operative techniques are followed by a high incidence of recurrent hemorrhage and mortality [2].

The pathology of stress ulcer is characterized by loss of superficial mucocytes and venous congestion with hemorrhage, mostly in the apical areas of the lamina propria. In more advanced lesions there is necrosis of the whole mucosa, and also involvement of the muscularis mucosa and submucosa, with marked passive congestion and spotty necrosis.

In shock states stress ulcer should be considered as one of the organic consequences of systemic failure due to energetic deprivation, secondary to the anaerobic cellular metabolism imposed by the hemodynamic response to hypovolemia, and to the cellular and vascular effects of lipopolysaccharide endotoxin in septic shock [3]. In the stomach, this energetic deprivation is more prominent in the superficial mucosal layer: in these epithelial cells, there is both a marked drop in DNA synthesis and a loss of RNA content. There are also qualitative changes in gastric mucus composition, as inferred from the decrease of glucosamine-synthetase activity [4]. Therefore, the mucosal barrier is damaged, and H^+ back-diffusion acts as disruptor of the entire mucosa. In addition, microcirculatory changes caused by vasoactive amines are present, and they have been correlated with degranulation of the mast cells.

Experimental Models for Stress Ulcer

The role of cellular energy deprivation in experimental stress ulcer was studied by us [6]: a progressive decrease of glucose levels in gastric mucosa was found; in addition a marked increase in the concentration of free fatty acids was observed, suggesting an alteration in the phospholipid composition of the cell membrane, due to the activating action of histamine on local phospholipases. This degradation should be taken into account to explain the decrease in mucosal cholesterol concentration.

Differences in pathogenesis between stress ulcer and peptic ulcer are also related to the role of hydrochloric acid and pepsin secretion. In stress ulcer, at electron microscopy, oxyntic and chief cells did not show important changes [7]; therefore, it is difficult to incriminate hydrochloric acid in the pathogenesis of these ulcers, since its secretion needs a large energetic expenditure by parietal cells: then, instead of showing the ultrastructural picture of a hypersecretory state, these oxyntic cells showed enlarged intracellular ducts and sparse microvilli. The most relevant finding in our study was a marked increment in the histidine-decarboxylase activity which explains the important participation of histamine in the pathogenesis of stress ulcer: histamine acts on submucosal microcirculation and, through the activation of phospholipase A, is responsible for the phospholipid component of cell membrane degradation, and for the inhibition of prostaglandin synthesis.

Somatostatin in the Clinical Management of Stress Ulcers

The high mortality of stress ulcers, especially when emergency surgery is involved, justifies the search for a new therapeutic approach. Thus, it was observed that somatostatin (SS) was able to reduce the incidence of experimental stress ulcer [8]: these results were interpreted as reflecting the action of SS on the oxyntic and chief cells, inhibiting the secretion of acid and pepsin [9]. An important participation of vasoactive amines in the beneficial effect of SS on stress ulcer has been proposed. By administering continuous intravenous infusions of SS [10], we found a marked reduction of the ulcer index, correlated with the decrease in the histamine and serotonin content in glandular gastric mucosa. This effect of SS on vasoactive amines is produced on mucosal argentaphin-like cells and submucosal mast cells, as inferred from an in vitro study, using the isolated stomach model [11]. Interestingly, SS can also stimulate gastric mucus output [12].

These effects of SS may also be useful in the management of gastroduodenal bleeding from peptic ulcer. However, in ulcer patients, the favorable effect of SS may be linked to its inhibiting action on hydrochloric acid and pepsin secretion, since these are primary factors in the pathogenesis of peptic ulcer disease, especially in duodenal ulcer patients. Endogenous gastric SS appears as an important factor in the mechanism of acid and pepsin secretory regulation: in a study carried out in patients [13] we have demonstrated with immunohistochemical and radioimmunoassay methods that patients with duodenal ulcer show marked reduction in the number of antral D cells and a significant decrease in antral concentrations of SS.

On the basis of these studies, we have recently published the results of the clinical application of SS in the treatment of severe upper gastrointestinal bleeding [14]. Most patients were admitted with gastroduodenal hemorrhage of peptic or stress ulcer origin (esophageal varices and neoplasias were excluded). This was a multicenter controlled trial, and patients were randomly assigned to two treatment groups receiving either SS or cimetidine plus pirenzepine. Successful hemostasis was significantly higher in the group treated with SS, the time to stop the hemorrhage was shorter, and less units of blood were required for hemodynamic compensation of the patients.

The beneficial effects of SS treatment should be critically analyzed. Indeed, a high percentage of patients will stop bleeding spontaneously. Therefore, carefully monitored trials should be conducted in patients with low chances of spontaneous recovery. Certainly, persistence of hemorrhage and failure to stabilize the hemodynamic situation will demand immediate operative correcture. In cases of peptic ulcer surgical hemostasis is indicated, whereas patients with stress ulcers may require a more radical intervention.

References

1 Greenberg, A.G.; Saik, R.P.; Bell, R.H.; Collins, G.M.: Changing patterns of gastrointestinal bleeding. Archs Surg. *120:* 341–344 (1985).

2 Kunzman, J.: Management of bleeding stress ulcers. Am.J. Surg. *119:* 637–639 (1970).

3 Garcia-Barreno, P.; Balibrea, J.L.: Metabolic response in shock. Surgery Gynec. Obstet. *146:* 182–190 (1978).

4 Menguy, R.;Desbaillets. L.; Masters, Y.F.: Mechanism of stress ulcer. Influence of hypovolemic shock on energy metabolism in the gastric mucosa. Gastroenterology *66:* 46–55 (1974).

5 Ozdemir, I.A.; Zimmermann, B.: Serotonin and restraint-induced gastrointestinal ulceration and microcirculatory ischemia. Surg. Forum *22:* 319–320 (1971).

6 Balibrea, J.L.; Canela, M.; Salva, J.A.; Puig, M.; Schwartz, S.; Rull, M.: Gastric mucosal energy metabolism in stress ulcer. Eur. surg. Res. *14:* 377–385 (1982).

7 Balibrea, J.L.; Merchan, J.; Gomez, J.; Alemany, J.A.; Aznar, J.; Fariña, J.; Barreno, P.G.; Fernandez, J.L.; Prado, J.: Restraint-induced stress ulcer. II. Biochemical and ultrastructural studies of gastric mucosa. Wld. J. Surg. *4:* 91–103 (1980).

8 Schwille, P.O.; Putz, F.; Thun, R.; Schellerer, W.; Draxler, G.; Lang, G.: Anti-stress ulcer and anti-secretory effect of somatostatin in rats. Failure to suppress serum gastrin. Acta hepato-gastroent. *24:* 259–265 (1977).

9 Gomez-Pan, A.; Reed, J.D.; Albinus, M.; Shaw, B.; Hall, R.; Besser, G.M.; Coy, D.H.; Kastin, A.J.; Schally, A.V.: Direct inhibition of gastric acid and pepsin secretion by growth-hormone release-inhibiting hormone in cats. Lancet *1:* 888–890 (1975).

10 Balibrea, J.L; Gomez, J.; Aznar, J.; Alemany, J.R.; Ruiz, J.; Fernandez, J.L.; Campos, J.M.; Barreno, P.G.; Avila, L.: Effects of somatostatin on gastric mucosal histamine and serotonin content in restrained rats. Eur. surg. Res. *11:* 8–14 (1979).

11 Balibrea, J.L.; Campos, J.M.; Alemany, J.R.; Gomez, J.; Aznar, J.; Corcuera, A.; Oller, B.; Negri, C.: In vitro effect of somatostatin on histamine and serotonin gastric concentrations. Wld. J. Surg. *5:* 440–441 (1981).

12 Johansson, C.; Aly, A.: Stimulation of gastric mucus output by somatostatin in man. Eur. J. clin. Invest. *12:* 37–39 (1982).

13 Torres, A.J.; Ortega, L.; Blanco, J.; Durango, R.F.; Merlo, F.H.; Suarez, A.; Cuberes, R.; Sanz, J.; Balibrea, J.L.: Antral gastrin-producing G-cells and somatostatin-producing D-cells in peptic ulcer. Virchows Arch. A *410:* 165–171 (1986).

14 Torres, A.J.; Landa, I.; Hernandez, F.; Jover, J.M.; Suarez, A.; Arias, J.; Cuberes, R.; Santoyo, J.; Fernandez, R.; Calleja, J.; Nisa, E.; Rodriquez, J. L.; Moreno, E.; Balibrea, J.L.; Somatostatin in the treatment of severe upper gastrointestinal bleeding. A multicentre controlled trial. Br. J. Surg. *73:* 786–789 (1986).

Dr. J.L. Balibrea
Department of Surgery
San Carlos University Hospital
University of Madrid
Madrid – 28040 (Spain)

Hormone Res. *29:* 106–108 (1988)

0301–0163/88/0293–0106$2.75/0

Prevention of Pancreatic Reactions by Bolus Somatostatin Administration in Patients Undergoing Endoscopic Retrograde Cholangio-Pancreatography and Endoscopic Sphincterotomy

Jose M. Bordas, V. Toledo, F. Mondelo, J. Rodés

Endoscopy Section, Liver Unit, Hospital Clínic i Provincial, University of Barcelona, Spain

Key Words. Pancreas exploration · Pancreatitis · Endoscopic sphincterotomy

Abstract. Mild pancreatitis is a common complication of endoscopic retrograde cholangio-pancreatography (ERCP) and endoscopic sphincterotomy. Knowing that a bolus injection of natural somatostatin (SRIF) dramatically reduces pancratic secretion, a study was conducted in 33 subjects undergoing invasive diagnostic procedures. A placebo (n = 16) or SRIF (n = 17; 4 μg/kg) were injected before cannulation. Enzymatic rise was observed in 16 (94%) subjects receiving placebo and in 8 (50%) injected previously with SRIF. In the former group 65% reported abdominal pain whereas only 19% had this complaint in the SRIF series. Results suggest that a bolus injection of SRIF may attenuate pancreatic irritation caused by diagnostic procedures or sphincterotomy.

Introduction

Endoscopic retrograde cholangio-pancreatography (ERCP) is a widely accepted procedure but complications are not rare. Among them, clinical pancreatitis is the most frequent, with an overall incidence of 1–7%. In spite of its generally benign evolution, hospitalization is frequently required. Pancreatic enzyme rise is very common after ERCP or endoscopic sphincterotomy (ES), currently without clinical significance although it represents a mild form of pancreatitis [1]. As a rule, amylase and lipase elevations are transient, appear immediately after examination and seem to be directly related to a local effect of the contrast agent, to the pressure of the injection and to the number of attempts. The peak of plasma enzyme elevations is usually observed 4 h after the procedure [1]. Some substances such as glucagon and aprotinin have failed to prevent transient hyperamylasemia and pancreatitis following ERCP, but an intravenous infusion of somatostatin for 4 h is able to decrease the magnitude of the pancreatic reaction, as shown by the lower degree of hyperamylasemia and hyperlipasemia after the procedure [2, 3]. Also, an intravenous bolus injection of somatostatin (4 μg/kg body weight) dramatically reduces the volume of pancreatic secretion with a concomitant increase of lipase and amylase contents.

These findings, the knowledge of the effects of somatostatin on the exocrine pancreatic secretion [4], and the difficulty in systemically administering prolonged intravenous infusions of somatostatin prompted us to assess the usefulness of a single bolus injection of somatostatin in preventing pancreatic irritation after endoscopic procedures.

Material and Methods

A double-blind study has been carried out in 33 patients undergoing ERCP or ES. All the patients submitted to ERCP or related therapeutic procedures received sedation and prophylactic antibiotherapy (clindamycin 600 mg, gentamicin 80 mg). They remained in bed at least 18 h after the procedure. Fasting is maintained at least for 6 h. Sedation was achieved by administration of pethydine, athropine and promethazine. The patients were randomly allocated to two groups. The control group received isotonic saline intravenously as a placebo, while the treated group received natural somatostatin in a single dose of 4 μg/kg body weight. The intravenous injection of somatostatin or placebo was carried out some 2–3 min before introduction of the endoscope, so that cannulation of the papilla and Wirsung duct opacification were achieved between 10 and 20 min after the injection.

The procedure was carried out with an Olympus type JF 1T10 endoscope. Contrast injection was carried out with a 10-ml syringe to avoid excess pressure, using hydrosoluble radiological contrast. The average duration of the whole procedure was 21 min, with a minimum of 8 and a maximum of 35. This time included both the diagnostic procedure and therapeutic maneuvers when endoscopic sphincterotomy was carried out. Serum amylase and lipase levels were determined 4 h after the procedure. Careful note was taken of the appearance of significant abdominal pain, requiring administration of analgesics during the following 24 h. Pancreatitis was considered to occur when there was a simultaneous appearance of upper abdominal pain, nausea and vomiting, associated with a marked reduction of peristalsis and a rise in lipase and amylase plasma levels. The chi-square test and the Student's t test were used in the statistical evaluation of the results.

Table I. Clinical data of 33 patients submitted to ERCP alone or associated with ES

	Somatostatin		Placebo	
	n	%	n	%
Number of patients	17		16	
Mean age, years	70		60	
Indications for the study				
Cholestasis	4	23	7	43
Cholelithiasis	4	23	5	31
Retained stones	7	41 n.s.	5	31
Papillary stenosis	1	5	0	0
Sex M/F	9/7		6/11	
Mean body weight, kg	65		58	
Total bilirubin, mg/dl mean	2.09		2.52	
Serum alkaline phosphatase (n < 190), mean	562		505	

Table II. Incidence of enzyme rise, abdominal pain needing analgesia, and clinical pancreatitis after ERCP

	Somatostatin group		Placebo group		Statistical significance
	n	%	n	%	
Overall patients (n = 33)					
Enzyme rise	8/16	50	16/17	94	p < 0.01
Pain	2/16	13	11/17	65	p < 0.01
Pancreatitis	–/16		2/16		–
Patients undergoing ERCP only (n = 20)					
Enzyme rise	5/8	63	11/12	92	n.s.
Pain	1/8	12	7/12	58	n.s.
Pancreatitis	–/8		–/12		–
Patients undergoing ERCP + ES (n = 13)					
Enzyme rise	3/8	38	5/5	100	n.s.
Pain	1/8	12	4/5	80	n.s.
Pancreatitis	–/8	–	2/5	–	–

Results and Conclusions

A total of 33 patients were evaluated. All had their pancreatic duct successfully opacified. Of these, 17 had been given somatostatin and 16 placebo. Eight of the group treated with somatostatin and 12 of the placebo group were only subjected to ERCP, marking a total of 20 patients, and the remaining 13 patients also had endoscopic sphincterotomy (8 in the somatostatin and 5 in the placebo group). Among the 33 patients, 16 received placebo and 17 were treated with somatostatin. Comparison of number, age, reason for the exploration, distribution by sex, body weight, total bilirubin and alkaline phosphatase, showed no significant differences between groups (table I).

Patients receiving placebo more frequently presented enzymatic rise (16/17 patients, 94%) than the somatostatin-treated group (8/16 patients, 50%) ($p < 0.01$) (table II). The percentage of patients who presented abdominal pain requiring analgesia was 65% in the placebo group and 13% in the somatostatin group ($p < 0.01$). Two of the 33 patients developed a slight pancreatitis which prolonged the hospital stay for 3 and 6 days, respectively. These 2 patients came from the placebo group (table II). Plasma lipase and amylase levels 4 h after the procedure are shown in table III. The enzyme levels in the somatostatin-treated group were significantly lower than in the placebo group (lipasemia $p < 0.05$, amylasemia $p < 0.05$).

Because ERCP as a diagnostic method involves less manipulation of the papillary region than endoscopic sphincterotomy, the 33 patients were divided into two subgroups according to whether they were submitted or not to endoscopic sphincterotomy. The group that only underwent ERCP included 20 patients. There were no differences between groups.

Table III. Enzyme levels 4 h after procedure

		Lipasemia (n < 40 U/l)			Amylasemia (n < 200 U/l)		
		somatostatin-treated group	placebo group		somatostatin-treated group	placebo group	
Patients undergoing ERCP only (n = 20)	Mean	125	336	t = 1.84	314	544	t = 1.80
	SD	194	149	p = n.s.	194	321	p = n.s.
Patients undergoing ERCP + sphincterotomy (n = 13)	Mean	112	248	t = 1.25	194	496	t = 2.59
	SD	177	210	p = n.s.	78	322	$p < 0.05$
Overall group (n = 33)	Mean	118	239	t = 2.30	254	530	t = 3.17
	SD	139	162	$p < 0.05$	155	312	$p < 0.05$

Among these 20 patients, enzyme rise and upper abdominal pain were more frequent in the placebo group than in the somatostatin-treated group, but the differences did not reach statistical significance. None of the patients developed pancreatitis (table II). Thirteen patients had an endoscopic therapeutic procedure in addition to ERCP. Eight of them were treated with bolus somatostatin and 5 received placebo. The incidence of enzyme rise and abdominal pain was recorded more frequently in the placebo than in the somatostatin group, but the differences only reached statistical significance in relation to plasma amylase levels which were significantly higher in the patients receiving placebo ($p < 0.05$) (table III). Two of the 5 patients who underwent papillotomy in the placebo group developed mild pancreatitis (table II).

These results suggest that the administration of a single bolus injection of somatostatin just before ERCP and ES may prevent pancreatic injury and pancreatitis, but in order to confirm these findings a larger number of patients should be studied.

References

1 Laugier, R.; Cicero, G.F.; Sahel, J.; Manganaro, M.; Sarles, H.: Effects of somatostatin on clinical, biochemical and morphological changes following ERCP; in Angelini, Usadel, Therapeutic effects of somatostatin, Serono Symposia Reviews, No 3, pp. 149–156 (Rome 1984).

2 Koch, H.; Belohlavlek, D.; Schaffner, O.; Tympner, F.; Rosen, W.; Demling, L.: Prospective study for the prevention of pancreatitis following endoscopic retrograde cholangio-pancreatography (ERCP). Endoscopy *7:* 221–224 (1975).

3 Masi, E.; Annessi, M.: Pancreas preservation by somatostatin in patients undergoing ERCP examination; in Angelini, Usadel, Therapeutic effects of somatostatin, Serono Symposia Reviews, No 3, pp. 177–183 (Rome 1984).

4 Susini, C.; Bomelaer, G.; Esteve, J.P.; Pradayrd, L.; Vaysse, N.: Effect of synthetic somatostatin on canine pancreatic exocrine secretion. Comparison with duodenal somatostatin-like-immunoreactivity (SLI) peptide. Metabolism *27* (Suppl. 1): 1341–1344 (1978).

Dr. Jose M. Bordas
Endoscopy Section, Liver Unit
Hospital Clínic i Provincial, University of Barcelona
Barcelona (Spain)

Hormone Res. 29: 109–111 (1988)

0301–0161/88/0293–0109$2.75/0

Size Changes of a Growth Hormone- and Prolactin-Producing Adenoma during and after Sandostatin Treatment

P.P. García-Luna[a], *A. Leal del Cerro*[a], *C. Santos*[a], *C. Montero*[a], *D. Acosta*[a], *E. Navarro*[a], *E. del Pozo*[b], *A. Gómez-Pan*[c], *R. Astorga*[a]

[a]Ciudad Sanitaria Virgen del Rocio, Sevilla, Spain; [b]Experimental Therapeutics Department, Clinical Research, Sandoz AG, Basle, Switzerland; [c]Servicio de Endocrinología, Hospital de la Princesa, Madrid, Spain

Key Words. Sandostatin · Mixed tumor · Volume reduction

Abstract. A 46-year-old woman with acromegaly and marked hyperprolactinemia was treated chronically with sandostatin (50 µg b.i.d. up to 100 µg t.i.d.). Plasma growth hormone (GH) was reduced by 90% of basal values and prolactin (PRL) dropped from initially 204 to 74 ng/ml. Serial CAT scans detected a volume reduction of the pituitary adenoma of 46.7%, but discontinuation of therapy was followed by re-expansion of the tumor. Tissue collected at transsphenoidal adenomectomy was examined by immunohistology and found positive for both GH and PRL. This characteristic would explain the dual hormonal response to the specific GH inhibitor sandostatin.

Introduction

Somatostatin was a promising agent for the treatment of acromegaly, but its use has been limited by its extremely short half-life. Recently, Bauer et al. [1] synthesized SMS 201-995 (sandostatin, Sandoz), a long-acting octapeptide analogue. This substance exerts a strong and prolonged inhibitory effect on growth hormone (GH) release, but only a short-term effect on insulin. The first report of Plewe et al. [2] demonstrated that sandostatin causes a long-standing suppression of GH levels in acromegalic patients, and prompted a series of clinical trials to evaluate the long-term efficacy of sandostatin as a therapeutic agent [3, 4].

Although both clinical and biochemical improvement after long-term administration have been reported in acromegalic patients, no substantial reduction in tumor size has yet been demonstrated. We present here the response to sandostatin of a previously untreated acromegalic patient with a GH-and prolactin (PRL)-producing pituitary tumor. This case demonstrates a marked reduction in tumor size after 5 months of treatment, and a clear reexpansion of the tumor which was observed 2 months after discontinuation of sandostatin administration.

Case Report

The patient was a 46-year-old woman with a 6-year history of obvious signs of acromegaly. Her menses had become irregular during the previous 8 months. She did not complain of headaches or visual abnormalities. On examination bilateral galactorrhea on expression was detected.

Average circulating GH was 68 ng/ml and exhibited a paradoxical response to a glucose load. No response to thyrothropin-releasing hormone (TRH) or GH-releasing factor (GRF) was seen. PRL profile (mean of at least three basal samples) showed hyperprolactinemia (204 ng/ml) with a moderate response to TRH (peak 392 ng/ml). Other parameters of pituitary function (ACTH, LH, FSH, TSH, cortisol, T3 and T4) were intact both basally and after appropriate stimuli.

The pituitary fossa was enlarged with erosion of the dorsum and part of the floor of the sella turcica. A computerized axial tomography (CAT) was performed and a bolus and an intravenous infusion of meglumine amidotriazate were administered as contrast medium. This CAT scan showed a pituitary macroadenoma, measuring 31 × 31 mm (area: 961 mm^2) (fig. 1a).

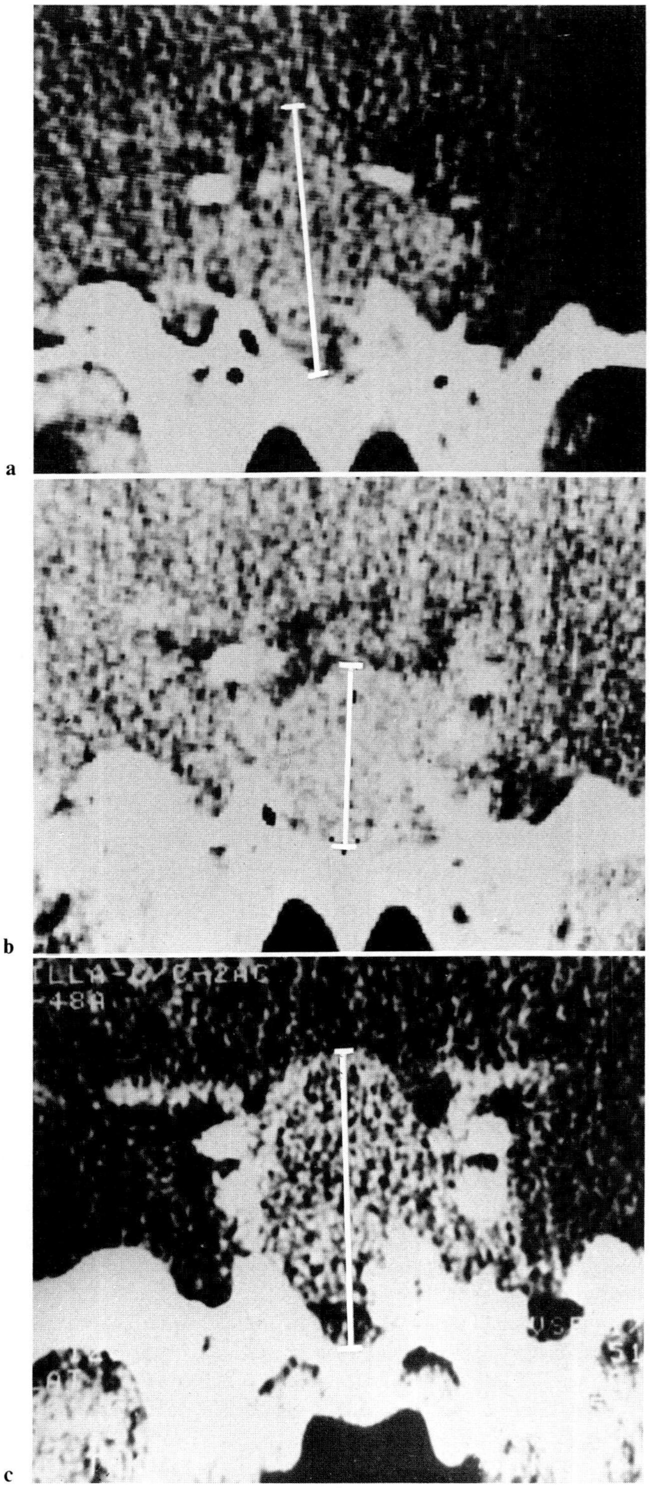

Fig. 1. Computerized tomographs recorded before (**a**) and during therapy with SMS 201-995 (**b**). There is a substantial decrease in tumor volume. Discontinuation of treatment (**c**) was followed by rapid increase in tumor size.

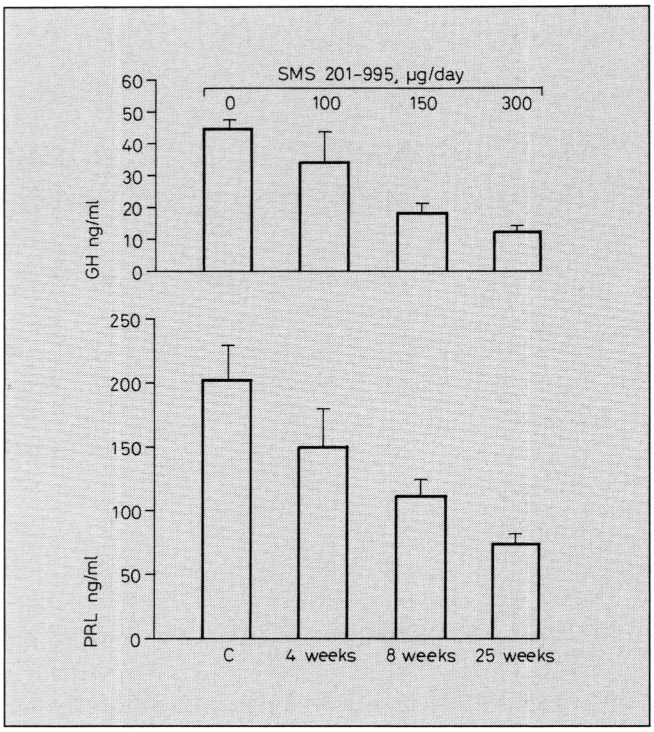

Fig. 2. Cumulative GH and PRL values throughout the 25-week observation period. There is a gradual, dose-dependent decrease in plasma concentration of both hormones.

The patient was treated with sandostatin according to the protocol approved by the local ethical committee. Initially, a dose of 50 μg s.c. b.i.d. (08.00 and 20.00 h) was administered for 4 weeks. The dosage was then increased to 50 μg s.c. t.i.d. (08.00, 14.00 and 20.00 h) for a further 4 weeks, and then the established at 100 μg s.c. t.i.d. (08.00, 14.00 and 20.00 h). The patient did not receive any other medication during the 25-week follow-up period. Sandostatin was well tolerated. A spectacular clinical improvement of her acromegalic features was observed. Galactorrhea disappeared by the fourth week of treatment.

The effects of sandostatin on plasma GH profiles are shown in figure 2. As can be seen, circulating GH levels were significantly reduced throughout the treatment period after each administration, up to 90% of basal values. Plasma PRL levels were also reduced following sandostatin administration. The mean PRL was 112 ng/ml by the 8th week of treatment and a further reduction to 74 ng/ml was evident 25 weeks after initiation of treatment. Other parameters of anterior pituitary function were not altered throughout the study.

A further CAT scan in the 25th week showed a marked reduction in tumor size. At this time, the tumor diameter measured 19 × 27 mm (area: 513 mm^2) (fig. 1b), which represents a reduction of 46.7% compared to the size previous to sandostatin administration (31 × 31 mm; area: 961 mm^2).

Contact with the patient was lost and treatment was discontinued for 2 months. A clinical and biochemical relapse was observed when she returned to the clinic. Another CAT scan showed that the pituitary tumor had increased to a size bigger than that at initial presentation (fig. 1c). A transsphenoidal adenomectomy was performed and immunohistological examination of the tumor was positive for both GH and PRL.

Discussion

The beneficial effects of sandostatin on the clinical signs and symptoms and on circulating GH levels experienced by our patient are consistent with data reported by other investigators [3, 4].

The effectiveness of medical treatment of secreting pituitary tumors should be evaluated in terms of inhibition of hormone secretion, remission of clinical signs of active disease, and, ideally, inhibition of tumor growth or reduction in tumor size. In this case, the efficacy of sandostatin was demonstrated by the following: suppression of GH levels to 10% and PRL levels to 36% of pretreatment values, a spectacular clinical improvement of acromegalic features, and a marked reduction in tumor volume after 5 months of treatment with a clear reexpansion of the tumor 2 months after discontinuation of sandostatin.

We are only aware of one previous publication describing a marked radiological reduction of a pituitary tumor by sandostatin [5]. This reduction in size may have been mediated by a direct pituitary effect of the peptide. Our patient had not had any previous therapy and it is possible that spontaneous infarction of the tumor would account for the change in size. However, we consider this alternative unlikely in view of the rapid reexpansion on cessation of therapy and the maintenance of the other pituitary functions after 25 weeks of treatment.

It is interesting that PRL levels were reduced and galactorrhea disappeared during therapy in our patient. Recently, Bassetti et al. [6] were able to detect the simultaneous presence of GH and PRL in the same secretory granule of a tumorous cell. The authors concluded that this characteristic would explain the dual hormonal response to stimulatory and inhibitory factors observed in some cases. Other authors have shown that plasma PRL was not affected by sandostatin in patients with pure GH-secreting adenomas, but was significantly suppressed in GH and PRL mixed tumors [7]. In our case, a similar tissue background can be assumed in view of positive immunohistological findings.

Both the sustained suppression of GH and PRL with the concomitant amelioration of acromegalic features and the clear reduction in tumor size, followed by reexpansion after discontinuation of treatment, justifiy the long-term use of sandostatin as a medical therapeutic agent in acromegaly and in GH/PRL mixed adenomas. Furthermore, the type of hormonal response in terms of GH and PRL reduction, may be of assistance in the characterization of the cellular lines involved, before surgery allows for histological examination.

References

1 Bauer, W.; Briner, V.; Doepfner, W.; Hall, R.; Huguenin, R.; Marbach, P.; Petcher, T.J.; Pless, J.: SMS 201-995. A very potent and selective octapeptide analogue of somatostatin with prolonged action. Life Sci. *31:* 1133–1141 (1982).

2 Plewe, G.; Beyer, J.; Krause, U.; Neufeld, M; Pozo, E. del: Long-acting and selective suppression of growth hormone secretion by somatostatin analogue SMS 201–995 in acromegaly. Lancet *ii:* 782–784 (1984).

3 Lamberts, S.W.J.; Uitterlinden, P.; Verschoor, L.; Van Dongen, K.J.; Pozo, E. del: Long term treatment of acromegaly with somatostatin analogue SMS 201–995. New Engl. J. Med. *313:* 1576–1580 (1985).

4 Tolis, G.; Yotis, A.; Pozo, E. del; Pitulis, S.: Therapeutic efficacy of a somatostatin analog (SMS 201-995) in active acromegaly. J. Neurosurg. *65:* 37–40 (1986).

5 Ducasse, M.C.R.; Tauber, J.P.; Harris, A.: Shrinking of a growth hormone producing pituitary tumor by continuous infusion of the somatostatin analog SMS 201-995. J. clin. Endocr. Metab. *65:* 1042–1046 (1987).

6 Bassetti, M.; Spada, A.; Arosio, M.; Vallar, L.; Brina, M.; Giannatasio, G.: Morphological studies on mixed growth hormone (GH)- and prolactin (PRL)-secreting human pituitary adenomas. Coexistence of GH and PRL in the same secretory granule. J. clin. Endocr. Metab. *62:* 1093–1096 (1986).

7 Lamberts, S.W.J.; Zweens, M.; Klijn, J.G.M.; van Vroonhaven, C.C.J.; Stefanko, S.Z.; Pozo, E. del: The sensitivity of growth hormone and prolactin secretion to the somatostatin analogue SMS 201-995 in patients with prolactinomas and acromegaly. Clin. Endocr. *25:* 201–212 (1986).

Dr. P.P. García-Luna
Ciudad Sanitaria Virgen del Rocio
Sevilla (Spain)

Hormone Res. *29:* 112–114 (1988)

0301–0163/88/0293–0112$2.75/0

Long-Term Management of Acromegaly with Sandostatin

George Tolis

Endocrine Division, Hippokrateion Hospital, Athens, Greece

Abstract. The present report illustrates the effectiveness of a long-acting somatostatin analog, SMS 201-995 (Sandostatin), in the chronic treatment of acromegaly. Daily doses of 50–300 μg were administered subcutaneously to 37 patients. Gradual dose increments induced a progressive GH decrease accompanied by a parallel reduction in plasma somatomedin C concentrations. There was a concomitant amelioration of clinical signs and symptoms throughout the investigational period. No escape phenomenon or tachyphylaxis was observed. It is concluded that chronic therapy with SMS 201-995 represents a promising medical alternative for the treatment of active acromegaly.

The introduction of the long-acting somatostatin derivative SMS 201-995 (Sandostatin, SMS) has represented a real progress in the noninvasive management of acromegaly. Previous reports have shown that daily subcutaneous administration of 100–300 mg in divided doses has improved this condition in a large number of patients, and clinical amelioration has been recorded in an elevated number of cases [1, 2].

The present study reports the findings collected in 37 acromegalic patients, 20 females and 17 males, treated chronically with SMS. Data were recorded from earlier reports and in part from de novo cases. In most instances conventional therapy with dopamine agonists and also surgery or irradiation had been used previously with little or no success.

Method

After basal evaluation, the patients were started on SMS therapy with increasing daily doses from 50 to 300 μg. The substance was injected subcutaneously in divided doses and the follow-up period was 4–50 weeks. Results of therapy were estimated by sequential measurements of growth hormone (GH) and somatomedin C (SM-C). In addition, circulating insulin, thyroxines and blood glucose were determined at different intervals during the treatment period.

An arbitrary scale from 1 to 3 was used to assess the clinical response on the basis of changes in soft tissue swelling, symptoms of neural compression, increased perspiration and depressive traits, among others.

Results

There was a dose-dependent GH decrease as depicted in figure 1. A daily dose of 50 μg was, in general, unable to reduce circulating GH in a significant manner. Furthermore, a mild rebound effect was observed in a few instances. However, gradual dose increments to 300 μg clearly showed a progressive and significant ($p < 0.001$) GH decrease accompanied by a parallel reduction in SM-C levels. Mean basal plasma concentrations of 56 ± 12 ng/ml had dropped to 16 ± 3 ng/ml when daily dosage was incremented to 300 μg, and in 22 cases GH reached, at least temporarily, normal levels (< 5 ng/ml). Figure 2 presents the correlation between the percentile GH fall and the SM-C reduction ($r = 0.77$; $p < 0.001$).

As expected, mean basal insulin was slightly elevated (28 ± 5 vs. 16 ± 3 mIU/ml in normal controls), unrelated to the presence or not of diabetes. At the end of the treatment period insulin levels had dropped to 22 ± 3 mIU/ml, but the difference was not significant. A detailed evaluation of the effect of SMS treatment on glucose homeostasis in acromegaly has been published elsewhere [3].

The effect of SMS on GH was accompanied by a definite improvement in clinical signs and symptoms of acromegaly. Shortly after initiation of treatment, all patients noticed improvement of some of the features and signs of the disease. When GH levels were normalized (< 5 ng/ml), complete disappearance of numbness,

1 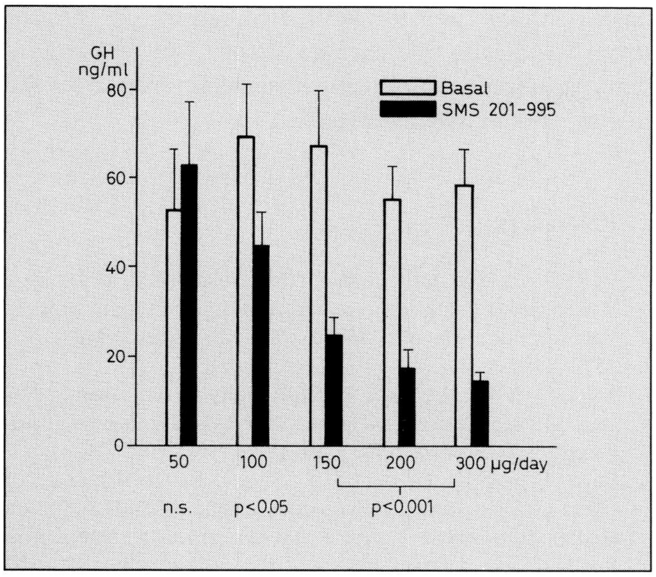

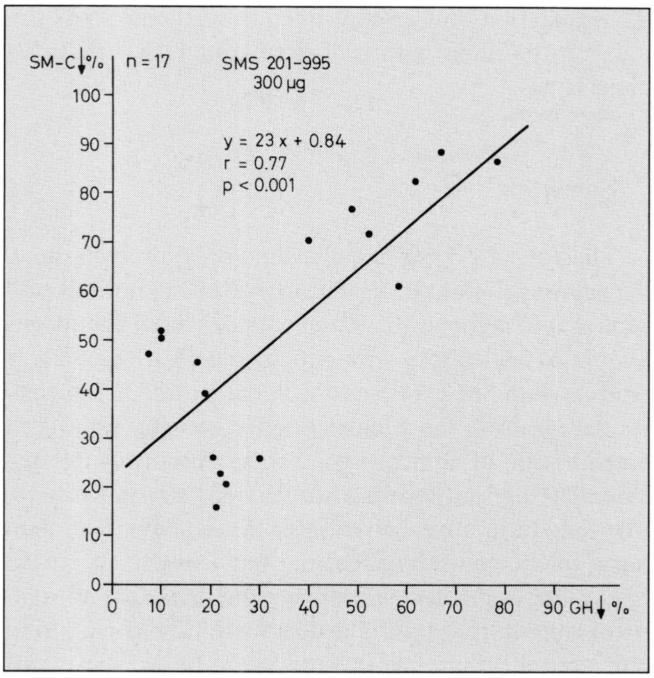 2

3 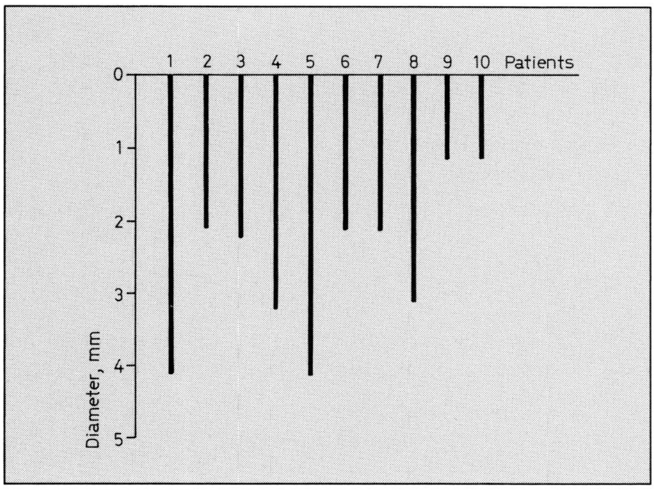

Fig. 1. Dose-related GH response in a group of 37 acromegalic subjects.

Fig. 2. Correlation between the percentage reduction in circulating GH levels and SM-C.

Fig. 3. Decrease of ring diameter in 10 evaluated acromegalic patients during the 6-week period of therapy with SMS 201-995.

paresthesias, headache, and perspiration occurred as early as 1 week after initiation of therapy. In those in whom GH levels were suppressed by more than 50% but remained above 5 ng/ml, clinical presentation also improved significantly. Symptoms of carpal tunnel syndrome disappeared in 2 of 3 patients so affected, despite non-normalization of GH levels. Increase in vitality and performance was observed in 10 of 12 patients. Figure 3 presents the changes in ring size recorded in 10 cases in which this parameter was considered. Reductions in diameter between 1 and 4 mm were recorded in all these patients.

Axial scans revealed a moderate diminution in pituitary tumor volume in 6 patients. Because of limited resolution of the scanning procedure used and relative small tumor size, assessment of radiological changes was difficult in a number of cases.

In general, medication was well tolerated. Two patients developed clinical steatorrhea as a result of decreased pancreatic and biliary tract function. Estimates of total fecal fat in another 10 subjects revealed substantial increments above baseline but still within normal limits. The hematological profile (red and white blood cell counts, hemoglobin, and hematocrit) and standard biochemistry studies (bilirubin, serum glutamic oxaloacetic transaminase, serum glutamic pyruvic transaminase, urea, creatinine, uric acid, and cholesterol) did not change during therapy. Serum triiodothyronine, thyroxine, and cortisol levels remained normal. No escape phenomenon or tachyphylaxis was observed on long-term administration, but discontinuation of therapy was followed by a prompt return of circulating GH to pretreatment levels.

Comments

These results confirm and extend previous data showing suppression of GH secretion by SMS in normal subjects and in acromegalic patients under basal conditions and following various stimulation tests [3, 4]. Good correlation with SM-C reductions in the treated acromegalics demonstrate full biological effectiveness, leading to amelioration of clinical signs and symptoms of the disease. The present report also provides strong evidence that long-term administration of this somatostatin analogue can be not only efficacious but also safe, as judged by the lack of relevant side effects and persistent normality of laboratory values. The demonstration of symptomatic control during therapy and the return of symptoms after treatment was discontinued indicate that this agent cannot offer a permanent cure. The significant improvement demonstrated in patients who had been previously unsuccessfully treated with irradiation or surgery strongly indicates that chronic therapy with SMS represents, at present, a promising medical alternative for the treatment of active acromegaly.

References

1 Lamberts, S.W.J.; Uitterlinden, P.; Verschoor, L.; van Dongen, K.J.; Pozo, E. del: Long term treatment of acromegaly with the somatostatin analogue SMS 201-995. New Engl. J. Med. *313:* 1576–1580 (1985).

2 Tolis, G.; Yotis, A.; Pozo, E. del; Pitoulis, S.: Therapeutic efficacy of a somatostatin analogue (SMS 201-995) in active acromegaly. J. Neurosurg. *65:* 37–40 (1986).

3 Pozo, E. del; Lamberts, S.W.J.; Sieber, C.; Gomez-Pan, A.: Effect of a long-acting somatostatin analog (SMS 201-995) on glucose homeostasis in type I diabetes and in acromegaly; in Reichlin, Somatostatin, basic and clinical status, pp. 293–302 (Plenum Press, New York, 1987).

Dr. George Tolis
Endocrine Division
Hippokrateion Hospital
Athens (Greece)

Hormone Res. *29:* 115–117 (1988)

0301–0163/88/0293–0115$2.75/0

Somatostatin Analog Treatment of Acromegaly: New Aspects

Steven W.J. Lamberts, Emilio del Pozo

Department of Medicine, Erasmus University, Rotterdam, The Netherlands; Sandoz Ltd., Basle, Switzerland

Key Words. Acromegaly · Sandostatin · Chronic treatment · Bromocriptine

Abstract. Ten acromegalics received daily doses of 200–300 μg of a long-acting somatostatin analog, SMS 201-995 (Sandostatin, SMS), for an average of 64 weeks. Basal mean GH values of 44 ± (SE) 7.8 ng/ml had fallen into the normal range at the end of the observation period (mean 64 weeks). This effect was accompanied by a substantial drop in somatomedin-C values. Reduction of pituitary tumor size could be documented in 3 of 6 patients. Whereas SMS did not affect high plasma PRL in 4 microprolactinoma patients, lactotrophs turned sensitive to this agent in mixed GH/PRL tumors. In a comparative study between SMS and bromocriptine, the former normalized circulating GH in 10 of 17 acromegalics in an acute trial, whereas bromocriptine was effective in only 5. A combination of both substances was effective in 2 of 3 patients who were insensitive to single drug administration. Cultures of GH-secreting tumor cells showed a statistically significant hormone decrease in the medium when exposed to SMS. However, in some instances, a diminution of the GH contents of the tumor cells was also observed, presumably as the basis for intracellular breakdown and clinical tumor shrinkage.

We reported earlier that treatment of 4 acromegalic patients for 8–24 weeks with 100–300 μg sandostatin (SMS 201-995) subcutaneously resulted in rapid amelioration of the clinical signs and symptoms and near normalization of laboratory test results in all patients [1].

Effect of Therapy for More than One Year

The above-mentioned study was extended to 10 acromegalic patients, 4 of them previously untreated, who were studied at regular intervals for 16–108 weeks (mean 64 ± 10). Sandostatin was administered daily in 2 or 3 subcutaneous injections of 100 μg (200–300 μg/day). Disappearance of excessive perspiration, paresthesias and headache was noted within the first 6 weeks of therapy. Soft tissue swelling also diminished or disappeared. The initially increased somatomedin-C (SM-C) levels normalized in 5 of these 10 patients (mean values 7.3 ± 0.9 U/ml before and 2.9 ± 0.7 U/ml at the end of therapy). The mean 24-hour GH concentration (mean of at least 20 samples collected over 24 h) fell from 44.0 ± 3.4 μg/l before to 7.8 ± 4 μg/l at the end of therapy. The course of these parameters before and at the end of therapy in these 10 acromegalics is shown in figure 1. GH levels from 2 to 6 h after 50 μg sandostatin before the start of therapy correlated significantly with the mean 24-hour GH concentrations after 16–108 weeks of treatment ($p < 0.05$).

The course of SM-C and mean GH levels showed a continuous further decrease during long-term therapy with sandostatin. Concentrations after 1.5–2 years of treatment were significantly lower than after 6–12 months of therapy ($p < 0.01$ and $p < 0.01$, respectively). Slight shrinkage of the pituitary tumor was observed by computerized tomography in 3 of the 6 patients in whom this could be evaluated. Transient clinically detectable steatorrhea occurred in 2 patients. Postprandial hyperglycemia was observed during sandostatin therapy in 8 patients, while in 2 patients with type 2 diabetes mellitus carbohydrate tolerance improved in 1 and deteriorated in the other.

Sandostatin is a highly effective medical treatment for acromegaly. Not only does clinical improvement rap-

1 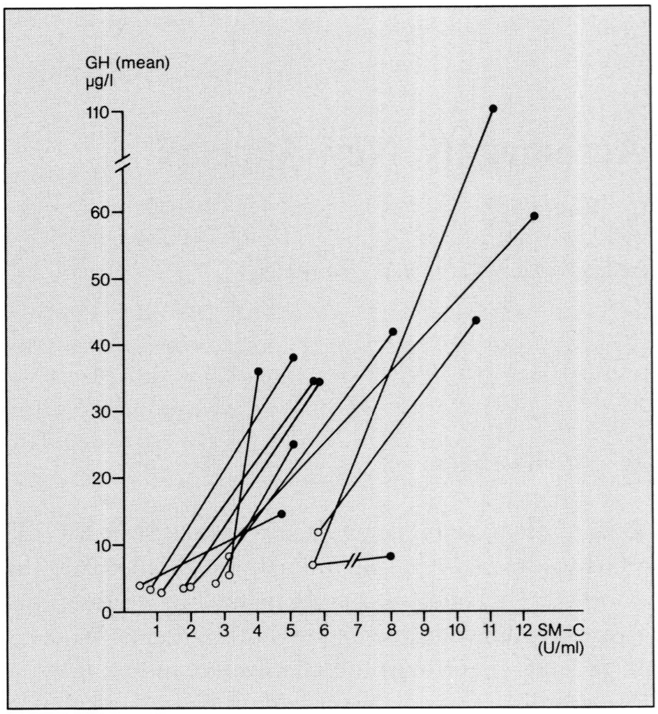

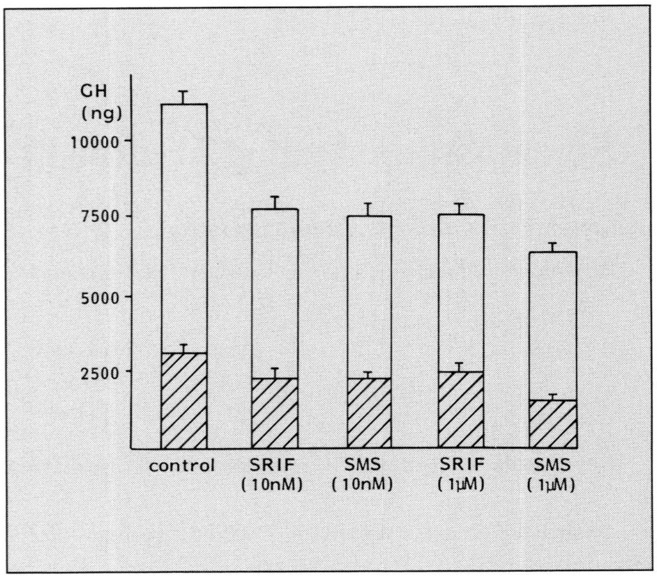 2

Fig. 1. Correlation between circulating GH and SM-C throughout the treatment period in 10 acromegalic subjects.

Fig. 2. GH concentrations in the medium and in cultured GH cells exposed to various doses of SRIF and SMS 201-995.

idly occur, but also the degree of inhibition of mean GH and SM-C levels further increases even after more than 1 year of therapy. No important subjective side effects were noted, making sandostatin an excellent drug for patients in whom acromegaly persists after surgery and as an interim treatment to shorten the period of clinical activity of the disease after irradiation.

Role of Prolactin

We investigated whether prolactin (PRL) secretion in patients with prolactinomas and acromegaly might also be sensitive to sandostatin, and whether co-secretion of PRL in acromegaly plays a role in determining the sensitivity of GH secretion to sandostatin [2]. The subcutaneous administration of 58 µg sandostatin did not affect high plasma PRL levels in 4 microprolactinoma patients. Therapy of 1 of these patients for 3 days with 50 µg three times a day did not affect PRL levels either. A single administration of 50 µg sandostatin in 22 acromegalic patients lowered plasma GH levels for 2–6 h to less than 5 µg/l in 14 patients and to less than 50% of control values in 16 patients. In 18 of these 22 patients the immunohistochemical picture of the pituitary tumor became known. Eleven patients had pure GH-containing tumors and 7 had mixed GH/PRL-containing tumors. In 2 of these latter patients there was evidence for GH and PRL being secreted by the same tumor cells. The sensitivity of GH secretion to sandostatin did not differ between the patients with pure GH or mixed GH/PRL-containing adenomas. Plasma PRL levels were not affected by sandostatin in the patients with pure GH-secreting tumors, but were significantly suppressed in 4 of the 7 patients with mixed GH/PRL-containing tumors. One patient with a mixed GH/PRL-containing tumor was treated daily for 16 weeks with 300 µg sandostatin. This resulted in normalization of both the increased GH and PRL levels. It is concluded that sandostatin does not affect tumorous PRL secretion in patients with prolactinomas. In acromegalic patients with mixed GH/PRL-containing tumors PRL secretion in some patients is sensitive to sandostatin, making these patients good candidates for chronic treatment with the analog. The simultaneous presence of PRL in the GH-secreting pituitary tumor or the presence of hyperprolactinemia in acromegalics does not affect the sensitivity of GH secretion to the somatostatin analog. A striking feature of the response to Sandostatin was an initial weight loss, thought to be due to abolition of the water and salt retaining action of GH. This effect has been well documented in rats [3].

A Comparison with the Effect of Bromocriptine

We compared the acute GH inhibitory effects of 50 µg sandostatin and 2.5 mg bromocriptine in 17 acromegalic patients [4]. Sandostatin suppressed plasma GH levels after 2–6 h to 5 µg/l or less in 10 of these 17 patients, whereas bromocriptine did the same in only 5. There was considerable variation in the responsiveness to both drugs in these patients, but the GH-lowering effect of 50 µg sandostatin was significantly greater than that of 2.5 mg bromocriptine. A combination of both drugs significantly suppressed plasma GH levels in 2 of 3 patients who were insensitive to both compounds when tested separately. It is concluded that most acromegalics respond better to sandostatin, while a few patients are more sensitive to the GH-lowering effect of bromocriptine. In addition, the combination of both drugs might be of value in few acromegalic patients who do not respond to either drug alone. These results are in agreement with long-term observations reported by Chiodini et al. [5].

The Mechanism of Tumor Shrinkage

As mentioned above tumor shrinkage during sandostatin treatment was observed in 3 of 6 acromegalic patients. The actual decrease in tumor size amounted to about 20–30%, which is less than that observed in most prolactinomas during therapy with bromocriptine. We investigated the possible mechanism of this shrinkage by exposing cultured pituitary tumor cells obtained from acromegalic patients during transsphenoidal surgery in vivo to somatostatin (SRIF) and sandostatin (SMS) (fig. 2). Cultured GH-secreting pituitary tumor cells exposed to sandostatin for varying periods of time (4 h–7 days) showed a variable, but in all instances during longer incubation period, statistically significant inhibition of GH release. In most tumor cells, this inhibitory effect on GH release was not accompanied by a change in the GH tumor cell content. However, in some tumors a sandostatin (and/or SRIF)-induced diminution of the hormonal content of the tumor cells was observed after 24–168 h. These changes either reflect an inhibition of GH synthesis and/or an increase in intracellular breakdown (crinophagy) of GH. This might be the basis for the tumor shrinkage which has been observed in about half of the acromegalic patients during long-term sandostatin therapy.

References

1 Lamberts, S.W.J.; Uitterlinden P.; Verschoor, L.; Dongen, K.J. van; Pozo E. del: Long-term treatment of acromegaly with the somatostatin analogue SMS 201-995. New Engl. J. Med. *313:* 1576–1580 (1985).

2 Lamberts, S.W.J.; Zweens, M.; Klijn J.G.M.; Vroonhoven, C.C.J.van; Stefanko, S.Z.; Pozo, E. del: The sensitivity of growth hormone and prolactin secretion to the somatostatin analogue SMS 201-995 in patients with prolactinomas and acromegaly. Clin. Endocr. *25:* 201–212 (1986).

3 Jørgensen, K.D.: Comparison of the pharmacological properties of pituitary and biosynthetic human growth hormone. Acta endocr., Copenh. *114:* 124–131 (1987).

4 Lamberts, S.W.J.; Zweens, M.; Verschoor, L.; Pozo, E. del: A comparison among the growth hormone-lowering effects in acromegaly of the somatostatin analog SMS 201-995, bromocriptine, and the combination of both drugs. J. clin. Endocr. Metab. *63:* 16–19 (1986).

5 Chiodini, P.G.; Cozzi, R.; Dallabonzana, D.; Oppizzi, G.; Verde, G; Petroncini, M.; Liuzzi, A.; Pozo, E. del: Medical treatment of acromegaly with SMS 201–995, a somatostatin analog: a comparison with bromocriptine. J. clin. Endocr. Metab. *64:* 447–453 (1987).

Dr. Steven W.J. Lamberts
Department of Medicine
Erasmus University
NL–3000 Rotterdam (The Netherlands)

Hormone Res. *29:* 118–120 (1988)

0301–0163/88/0293–0118$2.75/0

Somatostatin Analogs in the Management of Gastrointestinal Tumors

S. W.J. Lamberts

Department of Medicine, Erasmus University, Rotterdam, The Netherlands

Key Words. Sandostatin analog · Vipoma · Insulinoma · Nesidioblastosis

Abstract. Experience with SMS 201-995 (Sandostatin), a somatostatin analog, in the treatment of endocrine active gastrointestinal tumors is reviewed. Best immediate results were obtained in vipomas and insulinomas but a scape phenomenon was frequently observed. A positive and persistent effect was recorded in a case of nesidioblastosis. It was striking that good clinical control could be obtained in some instances despite insufficient suppression of hormone secretion by the tumor. This finding suggests peripheral actions of somatostatin and SMS independently of its primary effect on hormone release.

It has long been known that natural somatostatin is a potent inhibitor of hormone release in patients with peptide-secreting neuroendocrine tumors. The short natural elimination half-life of native somatostatin necessitates intravenous administration and precludes long-term therapy. In addition, a postinfusion rebound hypersecretion of hormones after stopping somatostatin infusion can be hazardous, especially in patients with insulinomas.

Chronic therapy with the somatostatin analog sandostatin (SMS 201-995) brought high hopes for a beneficial effect in this type of patients. In normal individuals sandostatin (50 μg subcutaneously) was shown to significantly lower basal and stimulated plasma levels of pancreatic polypeptide, secretin, pancreatic glucagon, insulin, and gastrin [1]. Wood et al. [2] reported the effects of chronic treatment of 7 patients with gut and pancreatic endocrine tumors with SMS 201-995 (100 μg daily). They observed dramatic improvement in endocrine-related symptoms with a decrease in, but no normalization of circulating tumor peptides. An exciting aspect of the therapeutic effects of sandostatin was the shrinkage of hepatic metastases in a patient with a vipoma who was treated for 7 months [3]. The symptomatic improvement observed in these patients during sandostatin therapy included healing of ulcers and diminution of diarrhea in gastrinoma, improvement of skin lesions in glucagonoma, decrease in number and/or intensity of flushes in serotonin-secreting carcinoids and decrease in stool volume with easy control of systemic electrolytic and water imbalances in vipoma. The beneficial action of sandostatin was readily shown especially in the syndrome of pancreatic cholera in vipoma patients [4, 5]. However, the diminution of the elevated circulating levels of pancreatic polypeptide, vasoactive intestinal polypeptide, neurotensin and motilin by sandostatin in these vipoma patients is probably not enough to explain the impressive clinical improvement. Therefore, a second direct inhibitory effect of sandostatin on the gut which slows transit time, increases electrolyte absorption and reduces jejunal secretion, has to be hypothesized.

Our observations in a 75-year-old patient with a metastasized vipoma were disappointing. She had very high VIP levels (2,000–2,500 ng/l; normal less than 100), severe watery diarrhea, hypokalemia and metabolic acidosis. An initial 50 μg dose of sandostatin was started and gradually increased daily. This resulted in a considerable reduction of stool volume and a normalization of serum potassium and acidosis thus eliminating oral cor-

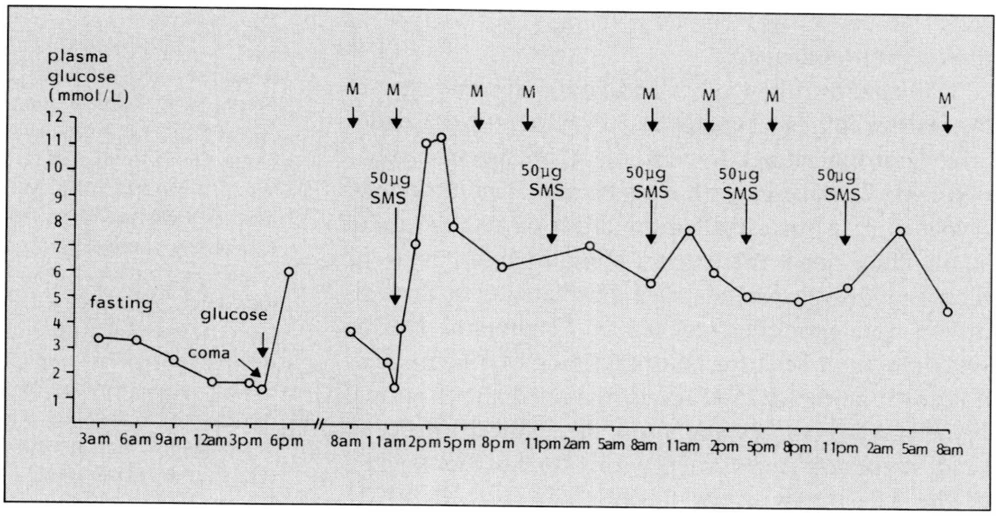

Fig. 1. Effect of repeated administration of sandostatin (SMS 201-995, 50 µg three times daily subcutaneously) on plasma glucose levels (M = meals) in a patient with a benign pancreatic insulinoma. With permission from Lamberts [9].

rection. After 8 days of treatment, however, diarrhea suddenly increased and severe hypokalemia and acidosis developed quickly over a period of 24 h. VIP levels, which had decreased during sandostatin therapy from 2,300 to 1,500 ng/l, increased to above 3,000 ng/l. Elevation of the daily dose of sandostatin resulted in another transient decrease in plasma VIP levels, concomitant with a decrease in stool volumes, which lasted only a couple of days. Thereafter, a second escape from therapy was observed, reflected both in deterioration of the clinical picture and augmentation of VIP levels. Such a sudden escape from sandostatin therapy with regard to both hormone secretion and to the possible effects on the gut is potentially dangerous, especially in vipoma and also in insulinoma patients.

The acute effects of sandostatin in 3 insulinoma patients studied in our clinic were rather promising [6]. The acute effect of a single subcutaneous dose of 50 µg sandostatin was compared to that of an infusion of natural somatostatin in 3 insulinoma patients. In 2 patients sandostatin suppressed circulating insulin levels by more than 50% and increased plasma glucose to hyperglycemic levels for 6–8 h. Although circulating insulin concentrations in the third patient were not suppressed, glucose levels became normoglycemic after a single administration of 50 µg of the analog. In contrast to the effect of natural somatostatin, no rebound increase in insulin levels occurred in these patients after sandostatin administration. Therapy for 2 or 3-day periods of 2 insulinoma patients with sandostatin (100–200 µg/day) prevented hypoglycemic attacks in these patients making this analog a promising tool in the preoperative management of insulinoma patients. Figure 1 shows the acute and long-term effects of multiple injections of 50 µg sandostatin on circulating glucose levels in a patient with a benign pancreatic insulinoma. This patient was treated with sandostatin (50 µg t.i.d.). During the 6 h following the initial dose, his clinical situation improved dramatically. After an initial hyperglycemic response, normal glycemia was maintained.

The potential use of sandostatin in the treatment of acute (neonatal) hypoglycemia is illustrated by our observations in a newborn child with nesidioblastosis [7]. Intravenous infusion of sandostatin in gradually increasing doses was accompanied by a fall in circulating insulin levels and restoration of normal glucose homeostasis. It can be expected that the analog will also prove to be helpful in the treatment of hypoglycemia of newborns of diabetic mothers and in other causes of neonatal low blood glucose.

From the preliminary results published on the effect of long-term therapy of endocrine pancreatic tumors with sandostatin [2, 4] several conclusions can be drawn. The effect of sandostatin in regard to the clinical aspects of the disease is in most patients excellent. In the majority of patients symptoms of hormone hypersecretion (diarrhea, skin lesions, flushes) are well controlled during chronic treatment with sandostatin and an escape of therapy occurs in only a few of them. The inhibiting effect of long-term sandostatin therapy on the circulating hormone levels, however, is less marked and escape phenomenon is frequent. Actual tumor shrinkage during sandostatin therapy has been observed in only a few cases [3, 8]. At present it is unknown why a secondary escape both clinically (minority of cases) and biochemically with regard to hormone secretion (majority of cases) occurs during long-term therapy of this type of tumor with sandostatin.

It is unknown how often and how quick this type of desensitization can be expected in patients with endocrine gastrointestinal tumors. In a prospective study involving 25 patients with metastatic carcinoid tumors, Kvols et al. [8] investigated the effect of 450 μg sandostatin daily for a median duration of more than 12 months. Flushing and diarrhea associated with the syndrome were promptly relieved in 22 patients. During this time, the 24-hour urinary excretion of 5-hydroxyindoleacetic acid (5-HIAA) levels remained above normal in most of them. Escape from the clinical effects of sandostatin occurred during continuation of therapy in 5 of the 22 patients whose flushing and in 4 of the 22 whose diarrhea was initially relieved. Thirteen of the 18 patients who had decreased 5-HIAA excretion to below 50% maintained such a decrease for 2–18 months. Thirteen of the patients had tumors that could be assessed objectively by linear or bidimensional measurement. In 4 of them (in)direct evidence of tumor shrinkage was found during chronic sandostatin therapy.

In conclusion, sandostatin is a major new therapeutic tool in the treatment of patients with neuroendocrine tumors, and studies presented until now illustrate its considerable therapeutic potential. However, only a few cases show evidence of an inhibition of tumor growth and often there is only a transient suppression of circulating hormone levels during long-term sandostatin therapy. The frequent unexpected appearance of desensitization or tachyphylaxis can cause severe clinical problems especially in vipoma and insulinoma patients. The enigma of good control of clinical manifestations of the disease despite insufficient suppression of tumor hormone secretion points to other direct peripheral actions of sandostatin; for example, on fluid transport through the gut and on gastrointestinal motility.

References

1 Kraenzlin, M.E.; Wood, S.M.; Neufeld, M.; Adrian, T.E.; Bloom, S.R.: Effect of long-acting somatostatin-analogue, SMS 201-995, on gut hormone secretion in normal subjects. Experientia *41:* 738–740 (1985).

2 Wood, S.M.; Kraenzlin, M.E.; Adrian, T.E.; Bloom, S.R.: Treatment of patients with pancreatic endocrine tumours using a new long-acting somatostatin analogue: symptomatic and peptide responses. Gut *26:* 438–444 (1985).

3 Kraenzlin, M.E.; Ch'ng, J.C.G.; Wood, S.M.; Carr, D.H.: Long-term treatment of a VIPoma with somatostatin analogue resulting in remission of symptoms and possible shrinkage of metastases. Gastroenterology *88:* 185–187 (1985).

4 Anderson, J.V.; Bloom, S.R.: Neuroendocrine tumours of the gut: long-term therapy with the somatostatin analogue SMS 201-995. Scand. J. Gastroent. *21:* 115–128 (1986).

5 Maton, P.M.; O'Dorisio, T.M.; Howe, B.A.; McArthur, K.E.; Howard, J.M.; Cherner, J.A.; Malarkey, T.B.; Collen, M.J.; Gardner, J.D.; Jensen, R.T.: Effect of a longacting somatostatin analogue (SMS 201-995) in a patient with pancreatic cholera. New Engl. J. Med. *312:* 17–21 (1985).

6 Verschoor, J.; Uitterlinden, P.; Lamberts, S.W.J.; Pozo, E. del: On the use of a new somatostatin analogue in the treatment of hypoglycaemia in patients with insulinoma. Clin. Endocr. *25:* 555–560 (1986).

7 Bruining, G.J.; Bosschaart, A.N.; Aarsen, R.S.R.; Lamberts, S.W.J.; Sauer, P.J.J.; Pozo, E. del: Normalization of glucose homeostasis by a long-acting somatostatin analog SMS 201-995 in a newborn with nesidioblastosis. Acta endocr., Copenh. *113:* suppl. 279, pp. 334–340 (1986).

8 Kvols, L.K.; Moertel, C.G.; O'Connell, M.J.; Schutt, A.J.; Rubin, J.; Hahn, R.G.: Treatment of the malignant carcinoid syndrome. Evaluation of a long-acting somatostatin analogue. New Engl. J. Med. *315:* 663–666 (1986).

9 Lamberts, S.W.J.: Non-pituitary actions of somatostatin. A review of the therapeutic role of SMS 201-995 (sandostatin). Acta endocr., Copenh. *112:* suppl. 276, pp. 41–56 (1986).

Dr. S.W.J. Lamberts
Department of Medicine
Erasmus University
NL-3000 Rotterdam (The Netherlands)

Hormone Res. 29: 121–123 (1988)

0301–0163/88/0293–0121$2.75/0

Treatment of Inappropriate Secretion of Thyrotropin with Somatostatin Analog SMS 201-995

P. Beck-Peccoz[a], *G. Medri*[a], *G. Piscitelli*[a], *S. Mariotti*[b], *A. Bertoli*[c], *A. Barbarino*[c], *M. Rondena*[a], *E. Martino*[b], *A. Pinchera*[b], *G. Faglia*[a]

Departments of Endocrinology, Universities of [a]Milan, [b]Pisa and [c]Rome, Italy

Key Words. Somatostatin · Somatostatin analogs · Inappropriate secretion of TSH · Hyperthyroidism · TSH-secreting pituitary tumors · Pituitary resistance · Thyroid hormone action

Abstract. Inappropriate thyrotropin secretion (IST) may originate from either neoplastic disease (nIST) or nonneoplastic resistance to thyroid hormone (nnIST). An inhibitory effect of somatostatin on TSH secretion has been documented. In an attempt to elucidate the possible therapeutic effect of this peptide on nIST and nnIST, a study was conducted in 7 such patients. Sandostatin (SMS 201-995) was administered in daily doses of 100 μg for several days to 1 month. Four patients with nIST responded with a fall in circulating TSH as well as α-subunit with concomitant normalization of free thyroxine and clear symptomatic improvement. In the 3 nnIST patients this effect was considerably less apparent and a partial TSH escape was observed on long-term treatment in 2 cases. The importance of somatostatin and its analogs in the management of thyroid malignancy is stressed.

Introduction

Hyperthyroidism secondary to inappropriate secretion of thyrotropin (IST) may result from either TSH-secreting pituitary tumors (neoplastic IST: nIST) or selective pituitary resistance to thyroid hormone action (nonneoplastic IST: nnIST) [1, 2]. Although the occurrence of both nIST and nnIST is very rare, the recognition of patients with IST is of great clinical importance since their therapeutic management completely differs from that of patients with more common forms of hyperthyroidism, such as autoimmune Graves' disease or autonomous thyroid nodules. Moreover, the therapeutic approach of nIST differs from that of nnIST, as the surgical removal of pituitary tumor is mandatory in the nIST, while treatment with agents that selectively suppress TSH secretion is indicated in the nnIST [3]. However, even the combined treatment with both surgery and irradiation failed to cure the nIST in 60% of patients reported in the literature [2]. Therefore, the treatment of nIST frequently relies on pharmacologic agents.

Since somatostatin has been documented to be one of the physiologic agents involved in the inhibitory control of TSH secretion [4], its use in treatment of both nIST and nnIST has been suggested, but never practiced because of the short plasma half-life (< 2 min) of the native neuropeptide. The current availability of a potent and long-acting analog of somatostatin (SMS 201-995, SMS) [5] prompted us to study its effect on serum TSH, α-subunit and free thyroid hormone concentrations in patients with either nIST or nnIST.

Materials and Methods

Seven patients affected with IST gave their informed consent to the study. In 4 of them, all previously operated on by transsphenoidal route, IST was of neoplastic origin and still active, as documented by neuroradiological signs of pituitary tumor, elevated serum α-subunit levels and α-sub/TSH molar ratio, lack of TSH response to both inhibitory (T3: 100 μg/day for 8–10 days) and stimulatory (TRH: 200 μg i.v.) tests. In the remaining 3 patients, IST was of nonneoplastic origin, as documented by the presence of qualitatively normal TSH response to the above tests, normal serum α-subunit levels and α-sub/TSH molar ratio. Clinical and biochemical features of hyperthyroidism were recorded in 3 cases of nIST (No. 1, 2 and 4) and in 2 nnIST (No. 5 and 6), while the remaining 2 patients were on L-T4 replacement therapy for previous thyroidectomy.

SMS 201–995 (Sandostatin®, Sandoz AG, Basel, Switzerland) was administered at the dose of 100 μg s.c. t.i.d. for 5 days in all patients, while in cases 2, 5 and 6 the treatment (100 μg s.c. every 12 h) was extended for 1 month.

Both in basal conditions and during SMS treatment, serum concentrations of TSH (ultrasensitive IRMA method: Sucrosep®, Boots-Celltech, Slough, UK), free T4 and T3 (direct method: Lisophase®, Sclavo, Siena, Italy), and α-subunit (RIA method: kind gift of NPA, NIDDK, Bethesda, MD, USA) were measured.

Results

The effects of short- and long-term treatment with SMS on serum TSH and FT3 levels are reported in table I. In all patients with nIST, serum TSH as well as α-subunit levels dramatically dropped with concomitant normalization of free thyroid hormone concentrations. In the 3 hyperthyroid patients, a clear improvement of symptoms and signs of the disease was observed. A steady euthyroid state was achieved in case 2 during long-term SMS administration, but the tumor size did not change, as shown by high resolution CT scan. In the 3 patients with nnIST, SMS administration had less powerful inhibitory effects on serum TSH and α-subunit concentrations, though free thyroid hormone levels normalized during the first days of treatment. In the 2 patients (No. 5 and 6) who underwent long-term treatment with SMS, a partial TSH escape from SMS inhibitory effects and a concomitant rise in serum FT4 and FT3 levels to pretreatment values, were observed.

No significant changes in glucose tolerance were observed, while transient untoward effects (nausea, abdominal discomfort, increased bowel frequency, steatorrhea) were recorded in cases 1, 3, 4 and 5.

Table I. Variations of serum TSH (mU/l) and free T3 (pmol/l) concentrations during SMS 201-995 administration (100 μg s.c. t.i.d.)

Case No.	Basal	Day 1	Day 2	Day 3	Day 4	Day 5	Day 30
Neoplastic IST							
1	4.3[1]	1.0	1.1	0.9	0.9	1.4	–
	11.7[2]	8.9	6.3	4.8	4.5	4.3	–
2	2.0	0.8	0.4	0.3	0.3	0.2	0.2
	21.0	15.6	6.6	7.6	6.8	6.9	5.2
3[3]	43.9	7.6	1.6	0.5	0.4	0.1	–
	6.1	5.7	4.5	3.7	4.5	4.5	–
4	28.4	7.5	5.7	5.2	3.9	–	–
	9.2	5.2	5.4	5.6	5.4	–	–
Nonneoplastic IST							
5	6.0	1.7	1.4	1.8	1.6	2.4	4.2
	10.6	7.4	5.1	5.1	5.2	6.6	10.4
6	32.2	26.4	27.2	27.8	29.8	17.0	40.0
	9.8	8.8	8.6	7.3	8.8	8.7	9.5
7[3]	215	150	185	224	110	116	–
	7.8	8.2	7.2	7.5	7.2	6.2	–

1 Normal range of TSH: 0.25–6.0 mU/l (n = 89).
2 Normal range of FT3: 3.8–8.9 pmol/l (n = 240).
3 On L-T4 replacement therapy for previous thyroidectomy.

Discussion

The results of this study clearly demonstrate the effectiveness of SMS 201-995 in controlling TSH and α-subunit hypersecretion from adenomatous thyrotrops and in restoring clinical and biochemical euthyroidism in patients with neoplastic IST. As documented in 1 case, the inhibitory effects of SMS persisted during long-term administration of the drug. In this case there was no reduction of the tumor size. However, the demonstration of possible SMS effects on tumor shrinkage in TSH-secreting pituitary adenomas will require treatment of a larger number of patients followed for a longer period of time.

On the contrary, the inhibitory effects of SMS on TSH secretion in patients with nonneoplastic IST were weaker and confined to the first days of treatment. Although the initial TSH reduction led to a decrease of serum free thyroid hormone levels within the normal range, they rose to pretreatment values when TSH escaped from SMS inhibitory effect. It is conceivable that the reduction in free thyroid hormone concentration might strongly stimulate TSH secretion, thus overcoming the inhibitory effects of SMS. This mechanism seems to be qualitatively similar to that operating in normal subjects or in acromegalic patients, in whom the thyroid state does not change during long-term SMS administration [6].

In conclusion, SMS appears to be a potentially useful therapeutic agent in the treatment of neoplastic IST, because previously available pharmacological therapy, i.e. dopamine agonists, such as bromocriptine, as well as thyroid hormones and their analogs, has been unsatisfactory [1, 2]. By contrast, SMS therapy in patients with nonneoplastic IST failed to selectively suppress TSH secretion, and thus does not appear to be a useful alternative to other pharmacologic agents, particularly TRIAC which is able to restore the euthyroid state in all patients with nonneoplastic IST throughout a selective inhibition of TSH hypersecretion and without any appreciable peripheral metabolic effect [2, 3].

References

1 Weintraub, D.B.; Menezes-Ferreira, M.M.; Petric, P.; Eil, C.; Beck-Peccoz, P.: Thyroid hormone resistance; in Labrie, Proulx, Endocrinology, p. 871 (Excerpta Medica, New York 1984).

2 Faglia, G.; Beck-Peccoz, P.; Piscitelli, G.; Medri, G.: Inappropriate secretion of thyrotropin by the pituitary. Hormone Res. *26:* 79–99 (1987).

3 Beck-Peccoz, P.; Piscitelli, G.; Cattaneo, M.G.; Faglia, G.: Successful treatment of hyperthyroidism due to nonneoplastic pituitary TSH hypersecretion with 3,5,3′-triiodothyroacetic acid (TRIAC). J. Endocr. Invest. *6:* 217–223 (1983).

4 Vale, W.; Rivier, C.; Brazeau, P.; Guillemin, R.: Effects of somatostatin on the secretion of thyrotropin and prolactin. Endocrinology *95:* 968–977 (1974).

5 Bauer, W.; Briner, U.; Doepfner, W.; Haller, R.; Huguenin, R.; Marbach, P.; Petcher, T.J.; Pless, J.: SMS 201-995: a very potent and selective octapeptide analogue of somatostatin with prolonged action. Life Sci. *31:* 1133–1140 (1982).

6 Lamberts, S.W.J.; Uitterlinden, P.; Verschoor, L.; Van Dongen, K.J.; Del Pozo, E.: Long-term treatment of acromegaly with the somatostatin analogue SMS 201-995. New Engl. J. Med. *313:* 1576–1580 (1985).

Dr. Paolo Beck-Peccoz
Department of Endocrinology
Ospedale Maggiore IRCCS
Paviglione Sacco
Via F. Sforza 35
I-20122 Milano (Italy)

Hormone Res. *29:* 124–128 (1988)

0301–0163/88/0293–0124$2.75/0

Plasma Alpha-Subunit Levels during the Treatment of Pituitary Adenomas with the Somatostatin Analog (SMS 201-995)

G. Sassolas, P. Serusclat, B. Claustrat, J. Trouillas, S. Merabet, R. Cohen, J.C. Souquet

Centre de Médecine Nucléaire, Service de Radiopharmacie et Radioanalyse, Hôpital Neuro-Cardiologique, Lyon, France

Key Words. SMS · Pituitary adenomas · Alpha-subunit

Abstract. The effect os SMS 201-995 (Sandostatin), a long-acting somatostatin analog, on different types of pituitary adenomas including α-subunit elevation is illustrated in this report. Treatment induced a fall in hCG levels in a woman with a pituitary adenoma producing only α-subunit. In 3 acromegalic patients, there was only a partial drop in GH and α-hCG. The same effect was observed in a woman with menopausal FSH and LH levels. SMS reduced plasma TSH and α-hCG in a case of thyrotropic adenoma. Two patients exhibiting FSH- and α-hCG-secreting adenomas did not respond to acute administration of SMS 201-995. More patients have to be treated before a definitive statement can be made on the usefulness of somatostatin analogs in the management of different types of pituitary adenomas.

Introduction

The α-subunit of glycoprotein hormones circulates unassociated as well as together with the β-subunits of TSH, LH and FSH. Serum α-subunit levels are elevated in parallel with the complete glycoprotein hormones, for instance in postmenopausal women, and in primary gonadal or thyroid failure.

In addition, α-subunit can be secreted by pituitary adenomas in association with FSH (in gonadotropin-secreting tumors) [1, 2], with TSH (in thyrotropin-secreting tumors), or separately in some rare cases of pure α-subunit-secreting pituitary tumors [3]. It may also be cosecreted with growth hormone, by the same cells and granules as recently demonstrated [4, 5].

The somatostatin analog SMS 201-995 (SMS) reduces GH secretion from somatotropinomas, as shown by in vivo and in vitro studies, and reduces in some instances the size of these tumors [5].

We report here the effects of SMS in different types of pituitary adenomas (PA). Indeed, we treated with SMS patients with acromegaly and abnormally elevated plasma levels of α-subunit. We also had the opportunity of observing the effects of SMS in a case of α-subunit secreting PA. In addition, we studied the effects of SMS in a patient presenting with a thyrotropic pituitary adenoma and in patients with gonadotropic pituitary adenomas.

Methods

Plasma Hormone Assays

GH, FSH, LH and TSH (Immunoradiometric method) were measured as previously reported [8].

The α-subunit was determined by radioimmunoassay using the reagents purchased from UCB (Brussels, Belgium) (hCG α-subunit iodination grade and antibody to hCG alpha). Results are expressed in terms of μg/l of α-hCG. Cross-reactivity of α-FSH, α-LH and α-TSH was given as 100% by the manufacturer in the α-hCG RIA (normal range: 0.5–2 μg/l; menopausal range: 2–7 μg/l).

Histological Studies

The pituitary tumors were studied by light and electron microscopy and by indirect immunofluorescence and immunoperoxidase methods.

The following antisera were used: anti-β-hFSH, anti-α-hFSH, anti-β-hTSH (kindly donated by NIADDK). As control these four antisera were preabsorbed with α-subunits (NIADDK); anti-17-39 ACTH (donated by M.O. Dubois); anti-hLH, anti-hGH and anti-hPRL and anti-β-endorphin (prepared by one of the authors: Bruno Claustrat).

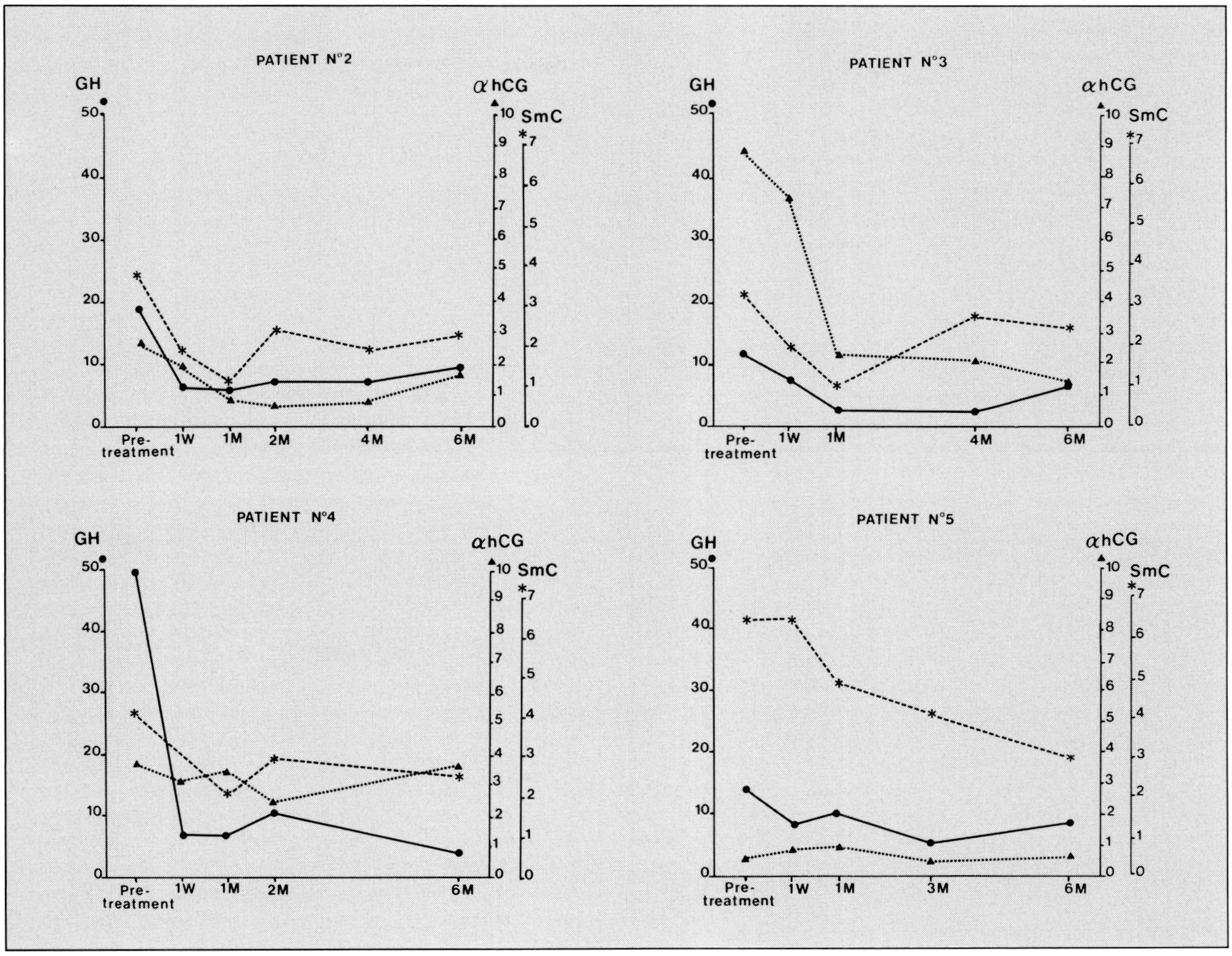

Fig. 1. Plasma levels of GH, Sm-C and α-hCG in 4 acromegalic patients.

Case Reports

Patient 1

A 49-year-old woman was treated by transphenoidal surgery in 1982 for a pituitary adenoma. Histological examination of the tumor revealed that it contained only α-subunit. Postoperative plasma α-hCG levels were elevated and CT scan demonstrated the presence of a supra-sellar mass. A Zollinger-Ellison syndrome due to gastrin secretion by a pancreatic tumor with regional lymph nodes was further discovered. This patient was then treated for 14 months with SMS (200 μg/day), with subsequent disappearance of epigastralgia and diarrhea, strong inhibition of basal and stimulated acid secretion, a fall in plasma gastrin levels and a decrease in plasma α-hCG levels (table I).

Patients 2, 3, and 5

Three acromegalic patients, 2 men (35 and 32 years of age) and a woman (51 years of age), had been treated by transphenoidal pitu-

Table I. Biological parameters before and during SMS treatment in a patient presenting with a pancreatic gastrinoma and an α-subunit-secreting pituitary adenoma

	Before SMS	Under SMS (200 μg/day)		
		3 days	4 months	10 months
TSH, μIU/ml	2	2		1.8
LH, mIU/ml	10	8		9
FSH, mIU/ml	6	7		8
α-hCG, μg/l	10.8	2.9	0.9	1
α-FSH (molar ratio)	26.3			
Acid secretion, mmol/h	18.3	1.7	0.7	
Gastrin, pg/ml	400	47	71	104

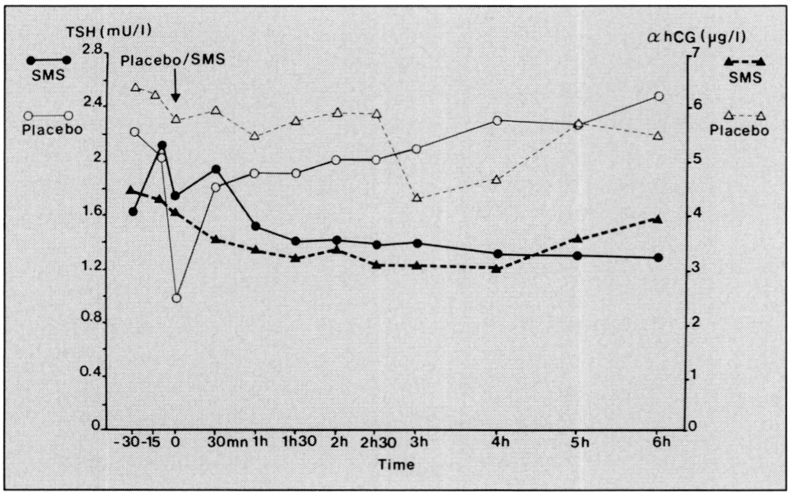

Fig. 2. Plasma α-hCG and TSH levels during the hours following the s.c. administration of SMS (100 μg) and placebo in patient 6.

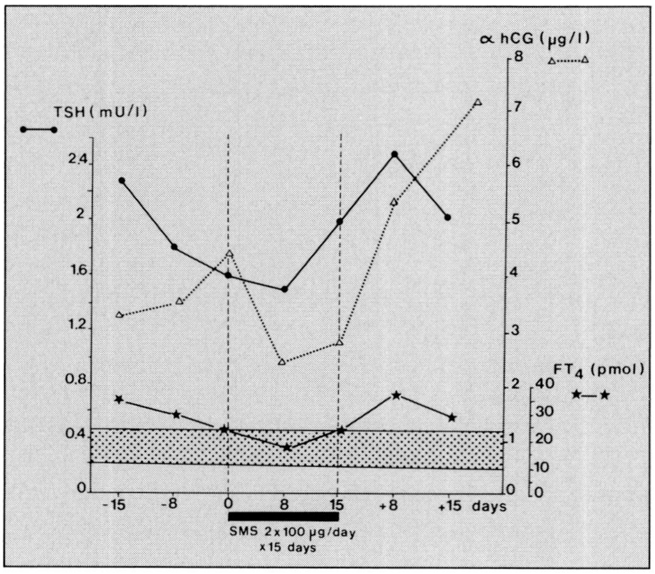

Fig. 3. Effects of a 15-day SMS treatment 200 μg/day on FT4, TSH and α-hCG plasma concentration.

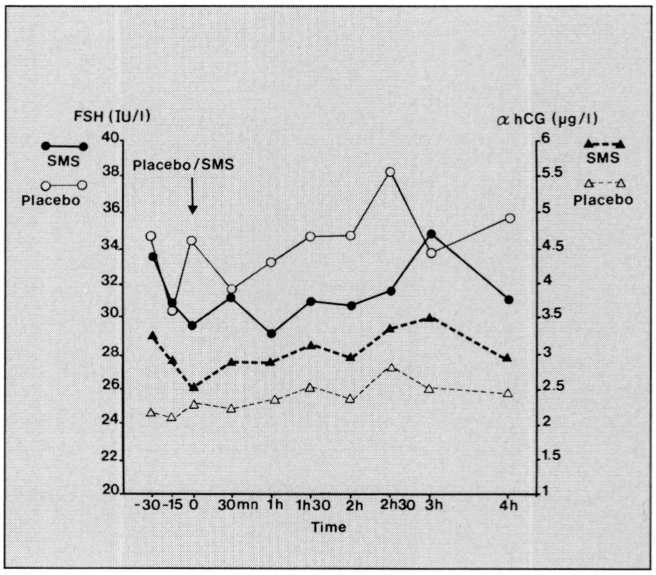

Fig. 4. Plasma FSH and α-hCG during the days following the s.c. administration of SMS (100 μg) and placebo in patient 7.

itary surgery. They remained uncured with abnormally elevated plasma GH levels, unresponsive to oral glucose administration, and there was evidence on CT scan of suprasellar and/or laterosellar tumor remnants.

Histological examination of the pituitary tumors had shown the presence of GH and α-subunit in the tumors of patients 2 and 3 and the unique presence of GH in the tumor of patient 5.

Plasma α-hCG levels were elevated in patients 2 and 3 (2.6 and 6.1 μg/l, respectively) and normal (0.5 μg/l) in patient 5 (whose gonadotropin levels were in the premenopausal range).

These 3 patients were treated for 6 months with SMS in doses of 2 × 100 μg/day for patients 2 and 3 and of 3 × 100 μg/day for patient 5.

Plasma GH, α-hCG and Sm-C levels were studied during different controls performed after 1 week, 2, 3 or 4 and 6 months of treatment (fig. 1).

Patient 4

A 45-year-old woman had been operated in January 1986 for a pancreatic endocrine tumor containing neither GRF nor GH. Acromegaly was then discovered at the time of surgery. Plasma α-hCG levels were elevated (3.6 μg/l); FSH and LH were in the menopausal range. A pituitary tumor with lateral expansion was demonstrated by CT scan. Medical treatment was chosen. The patient was treated for 6 months. The same biological parameters as for patients 2, 3 and 5 were controlled (fig. 2).

Patient 6

A 36-year-old woman had a pituitary adenoma, considered as thyrotropic given the moderately elevated free T4 levels, unappropriate TSH (comprised between 1.5 and 2.7 mIU/ml) and elevated α-hCG levels (5.2 μg/l), both hormones being unreactive to TRH.

Before surgery TSH, α-hCG and free T4 were studied: during the 7 h following SMS and placebo injection; during the 15 days of treatment with SMS (200 μg/day) and on the 15th day after withdrawal of this treatment (fig. 3).

Afterwards, the patient was submitted to surgery and cured by the removal of a thyrotropic pituitary adenoma, as confirmed by the postoperative normalization of hormones and by immunocytochemical study demonstrating the presence of α-subunit and β-TSH.

Patients 7 and 8

These 2 patients had persistent elevated plasma levels of FSH and α-hCG after the surgical resection of their tumor, considered as a gonadotropin-secreting PA after histological examination. They were studied only under acute conditions after subcutaenous injection of SMS 100 μg and placebo (fig. 4).

Comments and Conclusion

(1) The effect of SMS on plasma hCG levels in our first case was unexpected and fortuitously observed as this patient was treated by SMS for tumoral gastrin secretion. Moreover, we noted an impressive reduction in the suprasellar mass considered as a remnant of the partially removed pituitary adenoma. Further studies are required to confirm the antisecretory and antitumoral effect of SMS in this rare type of PA, usually classified as a form of gonadotropic adenoma. In addition, α-hCG production by the pancreatic tumor cannot be excluded.

(2) The parallel global effect of SMS on GH and α-subunit observed in the 2 cases with a proven co-secretion by the tumors was expected, and has already been suggested by others, in vitro and in short-term treatment. However, our treatment appears insufficient to normalize tumoral production of both hormones and plasma levels of Sm-C. It is likely that the doses of SMS used for these treatments (200–300 μg/day) were too low.

In patient 4, who had menopausal FSH and LH levels, the reduction of α-subunit was incomplete, suggesting that α-subunit was secreted in parallel with FSH and LH by the gonadotrophs, and thus was independent of the tumoral process. In patient 5, the plasma α-hCG level was normal, and SMS did not induce any change, as expected.

(3) SMS reduced plasma levels of TSH and α-hCG in the patient with thyrotropic adenoma, compared with placebo. A 15-day treatment had no spectacular effect. However, we observed a rebound after treatment, parallel in FT4, TSH and α-hCG levels. A recent report demonstrated the efficacity of SMS in a case of a PA-secreting GH and TSH [9] and in a case of TSH-secreting tumor [10].

(4) We did not observe any effect on FSH and α-hCG after a unique administration of SMS in 2 patients having pituitary adenoma secreting FSH and α-subunit. Longer administration of SMS should be required to obtain conclusive data.

In conclusion, SMS acts on the tumoral somatotrophs, inhibiting the release of GH and of the other hormones produced by these tumors such as TSH and α-subunit of the glycoprotein hormone.

Whether SMS really acts on other types of tumoral pituitary cells, remains an open question requiring investigation by different approaches both in vitro and in vivo.

References

1 Demura, R.; Jibiki, K.; Kuba, O.; Odagiri, E.; Demura, H.; Kitamura, K.; Shizume, K.: The significance of α-subunit as a tumor marker for gonadotropin-producing pituitary adenomas. J. clin. Endocr. Metab. *63:* 564–569 (1986).

2 Trouillas, J.; Girod, C.; Sassolas, G.; Claustrat, B.: The human gonadotropic adenoma: pathologic diagnosis and hormonal correlations in 26 tumors. Semin. diagn. Path. *3:* 42–57 (1986).

3 Klibanski, A.; Ridgway, E.C.; Zervas, N.T.: Pure α-subunit-secreting pituitary tumors. J. Neurosurg. *59:* 585–589 (1983).

4 Beck Peccoz, P.; Bassetti, M.; Spada, A.; Medri, G.; Arosio, M.; Giannastasio, G.; Faglia, G.: Glycoprotein hormone α-subunit response to growth hormone (GH)-releasing hormone in patients with active acromegaly. Evidence for α-subunit and GH coexistence in the same tumor cell. J. clin. Endocr. Metab. *61:* 541–546 (1985).

5 Horvath, E.; Kovacs, K.; Scheithauer, B.; Randall, R.V.; Laws, E.; Thorner, M.O.; Tindall, G.T.; Barrow, D.L.: Pituitary adenomas producing growth hormone prolactin and one or more glycoprotein hormones: a histologic, immunohistochemical and ultrastructural study of four surgically removed tumors. Ultrastruct. Path. *5:* 171–183 (1983).

6 Lamberts, S.W.J.; Oosterom, R.; Neufeld, M.; Del Pozo, E.: The somatostatin analog SMS 201-995 induces long-acting inhibition of growth hormone secretion without rebound hypersecretion in acromegalic patients. J. clin. Endocr. Metab. *60:* 1161–1165 (1985).

7 Lamberts, S.W.J.; Uitterlinders, P.; Vershoor, L.; Van Dongen, K.J.; Del Pozo, E.: Long-term treatment of acromegaly with the

somatostatin analogue SMS 201-995. New Engl. J. Med. *313:* 1576–1580 (1985).

8 Cohen, R.; Bouquier, D.; Biot-Laporte, S.; Vermeulen, E.; Claustrat, B.; Cherpin, M.H.; Cabrera, P.; Guidetti, P.; Ferry, S.; Bizollon, Ch.A.; Sassolas, G.: Pituitary stimulation by combined administration of four hypothalamic releasing hormones in normal men and patients. J. clin. Endocr. Metab. *62:* 892–898 (1986).

9 Beck-Peccoz, P.; Piscitelli, G.; Ams, S.; Ballabio, M.; Bosselti, H.; Giannastasio, G.; Spada, A.; Nissim, M.; Weintraub, B.D.; Faglia, G.: Endocrine, biochemical and morphological studies of a pituitary adenoma secreting growth hormone, thyrotropin (TSH) and alpha-subunit: evidence for secretion of TSH with increased bioactivity. J. clin. Endocr. Metab. *62:* 704–711 (1986).

10 Wemeau, J.L.; Dewailly, D.; Leroy, R.; Gueulle, I.; Grimbert, P.; Jaquet, P.; Decouls, M.: SMS 201-995: une thérapeutique nouvelle de l'adénome thyréotrope. A 79. 6th French Meet. Endocrinology, Nice 1986.

Dr. G. Sassolas
Centre de Médecine Nucléaire
Service de Radiopharmacie et Radioanalyse
Hôpital Neuro-Cardiologique
Lyon (France)

Hormone Res. 29: 129–132 (1988)

0301–0163/88/0293–0129$2.75/0

Influence of Somatostatin and Growth Hormone-Releasing Factor on Behavior

Clinical and Therapeutic Implications in Neuropsychiatric Disorders

Ramon Cacabelos[a], *Hisayoshi Niigawa*[a], *Maria D. Rodriguez-Arnao*[b], *Antonio Gómez-Pan*[c], *Tsuyoshi Nishimura*[a]

[a]Department of Neuropsychiatry, Osaka University Medical School, Fukushima, Osaka, Japan;
[b]Servicio de Endocrinología, Hospital G. Marañon, Madrid, Spain;
[c]Servicio de Endocrinología, Hospital de la Princesa, Madrid, Spain

Key Words. Somatostatin · Growth hormone-releasing factor · Neuropsychiatric disorders

Abstract. Administration of hypothalamic peptides has been reported to induce behavioral changes and to modify neurological functions such as locomotor activity and learning. Somatostatin (SS) and growth hormone-releasing factor (GRF) exert opposite effects on anterior pituitary secretion. Similarly, at the central nervous system (CNS) level, SS and GRF display antagonistic actions on behavioral parameters. The authors were able to confirm these effects in male Wistar rats by means of a computerized electronic maze measuring locomotor activity and learning. SS concentration is reduced in specific areas of the CNS in patients with late onset of senile dementia of the Alzheimer's type (SDAT). In early onset SDAT a GRF test elicits a growth hormone response much greater than that observed in normal controls of the same age or in patients with late onset SDAT. Thus, administration of GRF to patients with early onset SDAT has been followed by a significant improvement in locomotion, appetite, mental performance and social interaction. A possible therapeutic role of GRF in the management of patients with dementia remains to be explored.

Introduction

The somatotropinergic system (STS) (fig. 1) is the only neuroendocrine axis in which specific stimulatory and inhibitory neuropeptidergic regulators have been demonstrated thus far. In normal conditions, growth hormone-releasing factor (GRF) and somatostatin (SS) are the hypothalamic hypophysiotropic hormones responsible for the regulation of growth hormone (GH) secretion. At the same time, GRF and SS are influenced by central monoaminergic and peptidergic neuromodulators to optimize the functioning of the STS [1]. Recent investigations suggest that the functional structure of the STS characteristically represented at the peripheral level might exist in the CNS (fig. 1). Furthermore, SS levels are reduced in specific areas of the CNS in patients with senile dementia and are elevated in the neostriatum of patients with Huntington's chorea [2–4]. In addition, an abnormal rise of GH in response to GnRH or TRH has been described in several neuropsychiatric disorders [5]. It is likely that the central regulators of the STS (e.g. GRF, SS) influence higher activities of the CNS [1]. If this is true, it should be worthwhile to search for potential therapeutic uses of these neuropeptides in those neurological diseases in which the normal functioning of the STS is impaired.

Behavioral Effects of Somatostatin and Growth Hormone-Releasing Factor

SS is able to elicit electrophysiological, biochemical and behavioral effects of variable significance. For some authors SS inhibits the electrical activity of cortical and hypothalamic neurons while for others its effect is stimulatory. Epelbaum [4] suggests that SS excites neurons through a disinhibition of other neurotransmitters. SS inhibits noradrenaline and K^+-induced TRH release and enhances serotonin, acetylcholine and dopamine release in the brain [4, 6]. SS induces 'barrel rotation', apnea, tremors, and shaking, and influences thermoregulation,

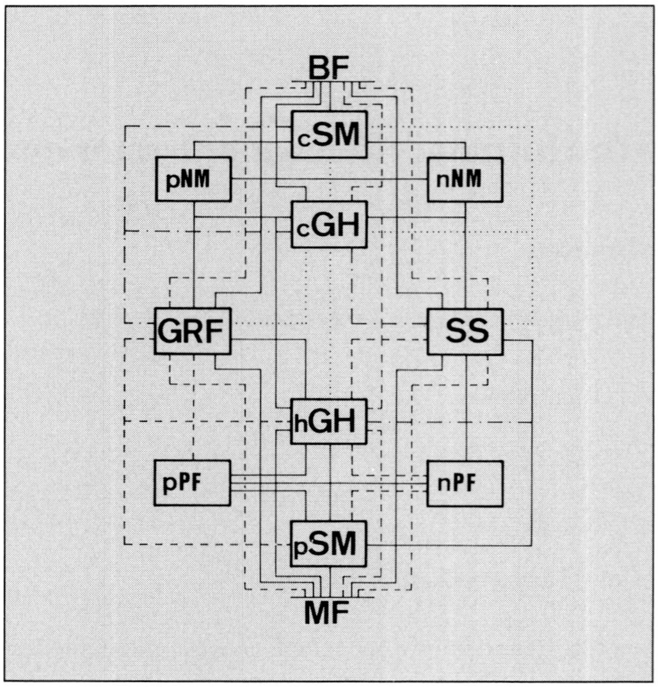

1

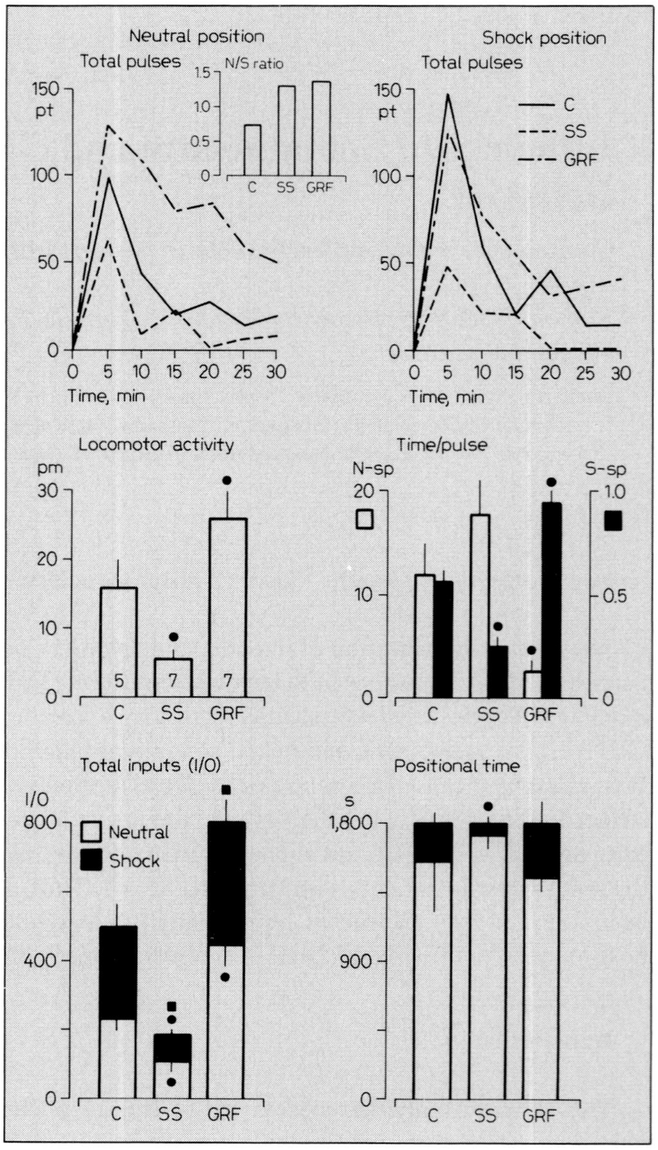

2

Fig. 1. Somatotropinergic system. Heuristic model for computer simulation. BF = Brain function; cGH = central growth hormone; cSM = central somatomedins; hGH = hypophyseal growth hormone; GRF = growth hormone-releasing factor; MF = metabolic function; nNM = negative neuromodulation; nPF = negative peripheral factors; pNM = positive neuromodulation; pPF = positive peripheral factors; pSM = peripheral somatomedins; SS = somatostatin. —— = Stimulation; – – – = inhibition; ······ = putative stimulatory effect; –·–· = putative inhibitory effect.

Fig. 2. Graphic representation of data recorded with the multi-computerized system (explanation in text).

locomotor activity, self-stimulation, scratching, writhing, retching, analgesia, sleep, electroconvulsive shock-induced amnesia, and active avoidance behavior. SS also exerts synchronizing, sedative, and weak antiepileptic effects, and suppresses both food and water ingestion in a dose-related manner [3, 4, 6, 7].

Data concerning behavioral effects of GRF are limited and controversial. In preliminary studies, Guillemin et al. [8] reported that intravenous bolus injection of high doses of GRF had a mild tranquilizing effect, if any, on rat behavior. With continuous EEG monitoring, Ehler et al. [see 8] observed that the i.c.v. injection of hpGRF-44 leads to the maintenance of a slow-wave sleep pattern and an increase in EEG stability. In contrast, Tannenbaum [9] reported that GRF induced long-lasting behavioral and motor effects. Recently, Vaccarino et al. [10] have demonstrated that rhGRF and hpGRF(1–40) in doses of 0.2, 2.0 and 20.0 pmol produce a marked increase in food intake in hungry rats.

Antagonistic Effects of Somatostatin and Growth Hormone-Releasing Factor on Locomotor Activity and Learning

To clarify whether SS and GRF display at the central level the same antagonistic effect that they have at the pituitary level, we have studied the effects of these neuropeptides on several behavioral parameters using the OUCEM-86® (Osaka University Computerized Electronic Maze). The OUCEM is a multicomputerized system which was developed by one of us (R.C.) in our laboratory. The system is integrated by the following components: a Programmable Electronic Platform (PEP) (620 × 620 mm) equipped with 48 photo beam sensors (OPX-T30); a Programming Panel (PP) (Model BECM-0064) for paradigm simulation; a Shock Generator Scrambler (SGS) (Model BSG-1065) to apply continuous or discontinuous electric current to the PEP; a Control Station (CS) (BEC 16-Bio Computer Control Station BCS-1105; Bio Medica, Ltd., Osaka) which processes inputs/outputs as an interface device to automatically computerize behavioral parameters; and a Computer System (NEC PC-9801F) with 1 megabyte Random Access Memory (RAM) for data processing and experimental setting.

Male Wistar rats (175–200 g) (n = 5–8 rats/group) received i.c.v. injections of GRF_{1-44} (Sumitomo, Japan), and SS-14 (Peninsula, USA) over a range of 0.1–10 μg. Then the rats were studied in the OUCEM under two different paradigms (e.g. open field and maze paradigms).

Study of Locomotor Activity in Novelty Conditions

The animals were placed in the PEP for 30-min periods and locomotor activity (LA) was automatically recorded in an open field paradigm. Total LA is represented as total inputs (I/O) including movements in the four-footed position (4F) and in the two-footed position (2F), grooming, rearing, and jumping activity, while linear (horizontal) movements (4F) are represented as pulses per minute (pm) or cm^2/min.

The i.c.v. administration of SS (1 μg) caused quantitative and qualitative changes with a significant decrease in LA (31.16 ± 6.90 pm vs. 20.88 ± 2.82 pm, $t = 3.08$, $p < 0.02$) while GRF (1 μg) induced a hyperkinetic syndrome characterized by compulsive, uncontrolled movements with an LA rate of 47.60 ± 5.35 pm ($t = 4.21$, $p < 0.005$) (control = 1,122 ± 248 cm^2/min; GRF = 1,713.6 ± 69.5 cm^2/min, $t = 18.73$, $p < 0.005$). These changes were dose dependent (SS: ED_{50} = 1.83 nmol, E_{max} = 6.10 nmol; GRF_{1-44}: ED_{50} = 99.1 pmol, E_{max} = 1.98 nmol; GRF_{1-29}: ED_{50} = 297 pmol, E_{max} = 5.95 nmol).

Effects of the Intracerebroventricular Administration of SS and GRF on Locomotor Activity and Learning in a Maze Paradigm

Using a maze paradigm in which the rats must learn to escape from a certain red area (shock area; SA) in order to avoid a continuous 1.5 mA electric shock, SS (1 μg i.c.v.) significantly reduced LA (17.12 ± 5.42 vs. 6.01 ± 1.45 pm, $t = 4.42$, $p < 0.005$) and GRF increased LA in a dose-related manner (26.66 ± 3.15 pm, $t = 3.40$, $p < 0.01$ at 1 μg; and 90.2 ± 8.4 pm, $t = 17.51$, $p < 0.005$, at 5 μg). The amounts of inputs (I/O) induced by SS was 103.5 ± 29.5 (control = 216.25 ± 55.19, $t = 8.49$, $p < 0.005$) in the neutral area (NA) and 77.14 ± 13.5 I/O in the shock area (SA) (control = 298 ± 40, $t = 1.26$, n.s.). GRF generated 459.35 ± 32.5 I/O in NA ($t = 18.13$, $p < 0.005$) and 340.5 ± 63.5 I/O in SA ($t = 9.07$, $p < 0.005$). The NA/SA (N/S) ratios for control, SS- and GRF-treated rats were 0.72, 1.33, and 1.35, respectively.

Computer values recorded are graphically represented in figure 2. Our results clearly show that GRF and SS exert antagonistic effects on LA in novelty conditions in both open field and maze paradigms. If we consider the N/S ratio as an index of learning, it seems that both SS and GRF improve learning abilities at doses of approximately 6.10×10^{-10} and 1.98×10^{-10} mol, respectively. However, since GRF induced a hyperkinetic syndrome in which the I/O rate as well as the positional time in SA were significantly higher than in the control group, it could be inferred that SS is more effective than GRF in improving learning. Indeed, the GRF-induced locomotor agitation (hyperkinetic syndrome) constitutes a serious drawback for the animal trying to differentiate and discriminate patterns in the maze.

SS and GRF in Neurological Diseases

In senile dementia of the Alzheimer's type (SDAT), the most prominent finding correlating with alterations in the cholinergic system is a selective loss of SS-like immunoreactivity in the neocortex and hippocampus [2, 3, 4, 14, 15]. SS immunoreactivity has been found in neuritic plaques [11] and neuronal tangles have been visualized in degenerated SS neurons [12]. In addition, SS binding sites are decreased in SDAT cortex and hippocampus [3].

In Huntington's disease the levels of SS in the neostriatum and nucleus accumbens are higher than in control brains [3, 13]. In Parkinson's disease, SS is reduced in the frontal cortex, entorhinal cortex, and hippocampus [11]. Nemeroff et al. [13] found that SS was reduced in the frontal cortex of schizophrenic patients, and several studies showed that SS is significantly reduced in the CSF of patients with unipolar depression [5, 6].

We have initiated a study program to investigate the potential therapeutic use of SS and GRF in SDAT [1, 2] and preliminary results show that GRF (1 μg/kg i.v.) elicits marked behavioral changes in SDAT patients. Locomotion, appetite, mental performance and social interaction are transiently (< 24 h) improved after a single dose of GRF in those patients with early onset SDAT and well-preserved physical conditions (< stage IV) (35%). In 60% of the patients with a good behavioral response to GRF there is a detectable GRF-induced GH peak in plasma at 60–90 min which is more significant in females than in males [1, 2, 14, 15]. This response is practically absent in healthy controls of the same age (> 60 years) and in late onset SDAT patients with severe dementia and deteriorated physical conditions (> stage IV) [Cacabelos, Niigawa, and Ikemura, unpubl. data]. In contrast, in patients with mental retardation and atypical psychomotor seizures (age = 20 ± 3 years; n = 6) there is systematically a flat response of GH to GRF and a tendency of the EEG to stabilize at 30–60 min postinjection (GRF_{1-44}: 1 μg/kg i.v.) [Cacabelos, Niigawa, Nagai, unpubl. results].

Concluding Remarks

Preliminary data seem to indicate that the STS is probably involved in some important facets of brain function. GRF and SS display antagonistic effects on behavioral parameters and partially improve learning in rats studied in a maze paradigm. The levels of SS are significantly affected in brain areas in degenerative diseases such us SDAT, Huntington's chorea, and Parkinson's disease, as well as in neuropsychiatric disorders like schizophrenia and depression. On the other hand, GRF is proving to be of utility in improving behavioral deficits in some cases of SDAT and mental retardation accompanied by epileptic seizures.

Acknowledgements

This study was supported in part by grants-in-aid from the Ministry of Education, Science and Culture, and the Ministry of Health and Welfare of Japan. We thank Dr. Kazuko Murakoshi, Dr. Junya Tanaka and Mr. Takahiro Tanioka (Yoshitomi Pharmaceutical Co., Osaka) for technical assistance, and Sumitomo Pharmaceutical Co. (Osaka, Japan) for generously supplying us with GRF_{1-44}.

References

1 Cacabelos, R.; Niigawa, H.; Hariguchi, S.: Hypothalamohypophyseal system and brain function. J. clin. Sci. *22:* 1108–1120 (1986).
2 Cacabelos, R.; Niigawa, H.; Ikemura, Y.: Neuroendocrine correlates in senile dementia of the Alzheimer type. Prog. clin. Neurosci. *2:* 231–247 (1986).
3 Beal, M.F.; Uhl, G.; Mazurek, M.F.; Kowall, N.; Martin, J.B.: Somatostatin: alterations in the central nervous system in neurological diseases; in Martin, Barchas, Neuropeptides in neurologic and psychiatric disease, pp. 215–257 (Raven Press, New York 1986).
4 Epelbaum, J.: Somatostatin in the central nervous system: physiology and pathological modifications. Progr. Neurobiol. *27:* 63–100 (1986).
5 Brown, G.M.; Koslow, S.M.; Reichlin, S.: Neuroendocrinology and psychiatric disorder (Raven Press, New York 1984).
6 Reichlin, S.: Somatostatin. New Engl. J. Med. *309:* 1556–1563 (1983).
7 Nemeroff, C.B.; Kalivas, P.W.; Golden, R.N.; Prange, A.J.: Behavioral effects of hypothalamic hypophysiotropic hormones, neurotensin, substance P and other neuropeptides. Pharmac. Ther. *24:* 1–56 (1984).
8 Guillemin, R.; Brazeau, P.; Bohlen, P.; Esch, F.; Ling, N.; Wehrenberg, W.B.; Bloch, B.; Mougin, C.; Zeytin, F.; Baird, A.: Somatocrinin, the growth hormone releasing factor. Recent Prog. Horm. Res. *40:* 233–299 (1984).
9 Tannenbaum, G.S.: Growth hormone-releasing factor: direct effects on growth hormone, glucose, and behavior via the brain. Science *226:* 464–466 (1984).
10 Vaccarino, F.J.; Bloom, F.E.; Rivier, J.; Vale, W.; Koob, G.F.: Stimulation of food intake in rats by centrally administered hypothalamic growth hormone-releasing factor. Nature, Lond. *314:* 167–168 (1985).
11 Morrison, J.H.; Rogers, J.; Scherr, S.; Benoit, R.; Bloom, F.E.: Somatostatin immunoreactivity in neuritic plaques of Alzheimer's patients. Nature, Lond. *314:* 90–92 (1985).
12 Roberts, G.W.; Crow, T.J.; Polak, J.M.: Localization of neuronal tangles in somatostatin neurons in Alzheimer's disease. Nature, Lond. *314:* 92–94 (1985).
13 Nemeroff, C.B.; Youngblood, W.W.; Manberg, P.J.; Prange, A.J.; Kizer, J.S.: Regional brain concentrations of neuropeptides in Huntington's chorea and schizophrenia. Science *221:* 972–975 (1983).
14 Cacabelos, R.; Niigawa, H.; Nishimura, T.: Neuroendocrine system in aging. Gerontopsychiatry *3:* 691–711 (1986).
15 Cacabelos, R.; Niigawa, H.; Nishimura, T.: Neuroendocrine function in psychiatric disorders and dementia. Jap. J. Neuropsychopharmacol. *9:* 13–49 (1987).

Dr. Ramon Cacabelos
Experimental Psychiatry Unit
Santiago University Medical School
Santiago de Compostela 15705 (Spain)

Progress in Surgery (ISSN 0079-6824), **Vol. 19**
Series Editor: E.H. Farthmann, Freiburg i.Br.

This volume will be of value to all those involved in the treatment of thyroid tumors interested in viewing a comprehensive, multi-disciplinary assessment of the present situation in the light of modern knowledge from the basic and clinical sciences.

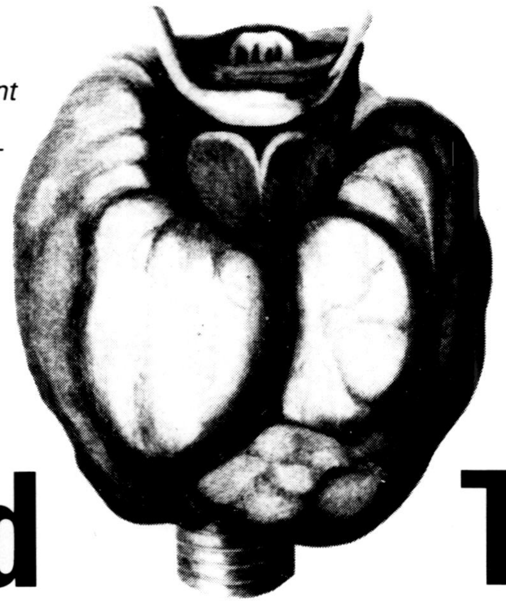

Thyroid Tumors

Volume Editors:
H.-D. Röher, Düsseldorf;
O.H. Clark, San Francisco, Calif.

In 14 invited chapters, this volume details the current status and recent developments and progress in the diagnosis and treatment of thyroid tumors. The book brings together the knowledge and experience of international experts in the various disciplines involved in the treatment of thyroid tumors. Papers describe progress in diagnostic methods and in the staging and grading of tumors. New developments in the surgical management of differentiated and undifferentiated tumors are outlined, and indications, effects and limitations of other treatment modalities are critically assessed.

Contents

Fields of Interest

Surgery; Biochemistry; Oncology; Chemotherapy, Cytology, Endocrinology, Radiology, Ultrasound

Progress in Surgery, Vol. 19
Thyroid Tumors
Volume Editors: H.-D. Röher, Düsseldorf; O.H. Clark, San Francisco, Calif.
VIII + 228 p., 44 fig., 36 tab., hard cover, 1988
SFr. 190.– / DM 228.– / US$ 126.75
US$ price for USA only (subject to change)
ISBN 3-8055-4713-7

KARGER

KI 87521